DEVELOPING MENTAL MATHS

WITH 7-9 YEAR OLDS

JON KURTA

Published by Scholastic Ltd
Villiers House
Clarendon Avenue
Leamington Spa
Warwickshire CV32 5PR

Text © 1997 Jon Kurta
© 1997 Scholastic Ltd

1 2 3 4 5 6 7 8 9 0   7 8 9 0 1 2 3 4 5 6

AUTHOR
Jon Kurta

SERIES CONSULTANT
Tamara Bibby

EDITOR
Joel Lane

ASSISTANT EDITOR
Lesley Sudlow

SERIES DESIGNER
Anna Oliwa

DESIGNER
Claire Belcher

ILLUSTRATIONS
Gary Swift

COVER ARTWORK
James Alexander/David Oliver
(Berkeley Studios)

Designed using Aldus Pagemaker

British Library Cataloguing-in-Publication Data
A catalogue record for this book is available from the British
Library.

ISBN 0-590-53764-4

CONTENTS

Mathematics does not exist in the world independent of the people who use it. It exists primarily in people's heads and is, therefore, a mental activity. The child's mental construction of numerical problems is thus a crucial aspect of developing numeracy.

Many adults in Britain today remember learning maths in primary school as a repetitive cycle of the teacher demonstrating a written method and working through an example on the board, then setting a page of practice 'sums' to reinforce that method. These methods or algorithms, many of which we still use, were developed so that the clerks and shopkeepers of post-Industrial Revolution Europe could accurately add and subtract, multiply and divide long columns of numbers.

We no longer need to work in that way, the mathematical demands of modern society are very different. We need to be able to read, and make sense of, a much wider range of numerical information: statistics including variable percentages and ratios, as well as the vast array of graphs and charts that has accompanied the computer revolution. Simply being able to apply the four rules of number in a narrow range of situations is no longer adequate.

BECOMING NUMERATE
We need to broaden our perception of numeracy, just as we have had to broaden our concept of what it means to be literate. The mathematics taught in primary schools should help children to develop an ability, and a willingness, to use mathematical skills and tools to tackle numerical problems in flexible and creative ways. A mechanical training in performing basic skills and operations is not enough.

Children need to be able to use mathematical skills and equipment with equal facility in a wide range of contexts. People who are fully numerate are able to:
● perform number operations with measures and money as well as in the abstract (as pages of 'sums' with no real context);
● deal with numerical information presented in a variety of ways including diagrams, graphs, tables and charts;
● make decisions about whether to work mentally, on paper or with a calculator, depending on the degree of accuracy needed and the complexity of the task.

THE IMPORTANCE OF MENTAL CALCULATION
Over a period of many years, school inspectors have called for increased attention to be given to mental calculation. They have highlighted an over-reliance on counting methods among older Key Stage 2 children, as well as an inability to make sensible estimates (see HMCI *Annual Report* 1994/95, for example). It has been suggested that teachers need to help children develop mathematical language skills, as well as a 'feel for number', by using discussion to challenge their understanding. Further emphasis has been placed upon the importance of identifying, analysing and correcting errors and misconceptions in the understanding of number (see *The Teaching and Learning of Number in Primary Schools, Mathematics AT2*, 1993).

Recently, the Government became so concerned about the apparent drop in standards in numeracy that it set up twelve national centres to work with schools and teachers to raise standards of attainment (the National Numeracy Project). This concern has been echoed by public anxiety and calls for a return to the teaching of mental maths. These concerns are not new, and were particularly well articulated in the Cockcroft Report (1982). Many of the points that Cockcroft made continue to be repeated in current public debate:

255 *We believe that the decline of mental and oral work within mathematics classrooms represents a failure to recognise the central place which working 'done in the head' occupies throughout mathematics. Even when using traditional methods of recording calculations on paper, the written record is usually based on steps which are done mentally.*

When working on 'everyday maths', people who are 'mathematically effective' tend not to use the standard written methods they were taught in school: they work mentally and use personal methods. The Cockcroft Report points out:

256 *Although many pupils come to realise by themselves that methods which may be convenient on paper are often not well suited to use 'in their heads'... in the case of many other pupils it is necessary for the teacher to point out explicitly and to discuss at length the variety of methods which it is possible to use...*

Although many people *do* develop flexible methods on their own, this has generally been achieved *in spite of* the teaching they received: the development of a range of flexible methods is rarely

encouraged in an explicit way. Children need to be taught to develop a variety of flexible methods which can be used appropriately in different contexts. However, as <u>Cockcroft</u> goes on to say:

> *...no attempt should be made to force a single 'proper method' of performing mental calculations; pupils should be encouraged to make use of whatever methods suit them best. Teachers should also encourage pupils to reflect upon the methods which they develop for themselves so that facility in mental computation can be consolidated and extended.*

The National Curriculum (1995) states that:

> *pupils should be given opportunities to develop flexible methods of working with number, orally and mentally.*
> *(KS1 Number 1a)*

> *pupils should be given opportunities to develop flexible methods of computation and recording, and use them with understanding; and develop the skills needed for accurate and appropriate use of equipment. (KS2 Number 1a and c)*

and, more specifically:

> *pupils should be taught to develop a variety of mental methods of computation with whole numbers to 100, and explain patterns used; extend mental methods to develop a range of non-calculator methods of computation that involve addition and subtraction of whole numbers, progressing to methods for multiplication and division of up to three-digit by two-digit whole numbers. (KS2 Number 3d)*

The Scottish Guidelines for Mathematics 5–14 considers 'using mental methods' as a discrete issue in maths teaching. It exemplifies the range of methods that might be used for straightforward mental calculation, and goes on to state that:

> *It is important, then, to recognise that when calculating mentally we usually make use of different methods from those we have used for written calculations. We should encourage pupils to develop and practise flexible mental approaches. One way of doing this is through class or group discussion of the variety of different ways of carrying out particular calculations. (Section b)*

With regard to school schemes of work, the Non-Statutory Guidance for the National Curriculum (1989) states that:

> 511 *Activities should encourage pupils to use mental arithmetic and to become confident in the use of a range of mathematical tools.*
> ● *The ability to use mental arithmetic in everyday life and work is very important. This includes the vital skills of estimating results in advance, and of checking answers mentally for accuracy and reasonableness.*
> ● *Activities should provide opportunities for pupils to develop skills in selecting and using a wide range of mathematical tools – constructional kits, drawing instruments, measuring equipment, calculating aids, electronic calculators and micro-computers. They should also help pupils to select with confidence the most appropriate ways to tackle different problems.*

The effective and appropriate use of these mathematical tools requires an understanding of likely outcomes and an ability to estimate. The ability to select and use efficient mathematical tools is a skill needed throughout life. As an adult, for example, I might need to keep track of money in a bank account. A variety of tools are available to help me: from spreadsheets to account books, calculators and bits of paper. The level of detail at which I need to keep track of the money in the account will vary according to circumstances. If, for example, I am saving for a holiday, a simple statement of the money available in a savings account written on a piece of paper will probably be adequate. If, however, the account is that of a small business with overheads, bills outstanding and suppliers to be paid, then the information would be more effectively conveyed by a spreadsheet.

MATHEMATICAL TOOLS AND MENTAL MATHEMATICS

At first sight, it may seem a contradiction to talk about mental mathematics in the same context as the use of mathematical tools (such as calculators) and paper and pencil. However, they can be used together, for different aspects of the same task.

For example, imagine the task of estimating the cost of a class visit to a museum: public transport, entrance fees, reduced rates for a group booking and so on. You would undoubtedly make jottings on a scrap of paper, rounding up or down to keep the numbers manageable, working out the calculations mentally but keeping note of the stages as there is too much information to hold in your head. The *mathematics* is being worked out mentally (you are not using paper and pencil algorithms), but the paper and pencil are there to 'extend your mental screen' – to assist memory. Without the paper and pencil, the task could well be unmanageable.

Alternatively, a calculator may be used when the numbers are 'fiddly' or when repeated use of the same operation on several numbers makes the memory facility a convenient aid to calculation. In such cases, the steps may be straightforward but long, and the calculations may be tedious to perform. The maths required includes both repetitive calculations *and* an understanding of the steps to be taken. When deciding whether calculators would be appropriate in a problem-solving task, the teacher needs to ask: 'What do I want the class to get out of this activity – practice doing calculations or practice in deciding what mathematics to use?'

FACTS AND FIGURES

Recent research[1] indicates that 'knowing by heart' and 'figuring out' can support each other. Working successfully in your head involves using things that you already know to derive new information. In time, things that you once had to work out are added to the repertoire of things

that you know. As your stock of known facts increases, it adds to the range of ways available to you to work things out.

Consider the differences between these four ways of working out 7×7, and what needs to be known for each method.

- Multiplication can be carried out by repeated addition:

$$7 + 7 + 7 + 7 + 7 + 7 + 7 = 49$$

- Multiplication of larger numbers can be built up in smaller steps by doubling and subtracting:

$2 \times 7 = 14$		
double	$2 \times (2 \times 7) = 28$	ie 4×7
double	$2 \times (4 \times 7) = 56$	ie 8×7
subtract	$56 - 7 = 49$	ie 7×7

- Multiplication of larger numbers can also be built up in smaller steps by doubling and adding:

$3 \times 7 = 21$		
double	$2 \times (3 \times 7) = 42$	ie 6×7
add	$42 + 7 = 49$	ie 7×7

- Multiplication of larger numbers can also be built up in smaller steps by using complements of the numbers:

$$7 = 5 + 2, \text{ so}$$
$$(5 \times 7) + (2 \times 7) = 35 + 14 = 49$$

Each of these methods uses known facts and procedures to 'figure out' new information. Not everyone feels able to make such use of the number facts they know. Often those who are insecure about their mathematical knowledge would rather use familiar counting methods, which seem safer. Many children become very adept at developing counting strategies. In the end, however, these are slow, cumbersome and inefficient, so pupils need to be encouraged away from them.

Children need to be given the scope to develop ways of working which allow them to increase their store of known facts and of strategies for using these to derive new information. They need to be shown ways to develop more efficient and effective strategies, thus moving beyond a reliance on counting. This requires them to take risks, so they will need a 'safe' environment: one where their ideas are valued and creative approaches are actively encouraged.

THE PLACE OF WRITTEN WORK

In helping children to build upon what they know, the facts of which they already have command will need to be tracked. If they are being challenged to work mentally, most children will develop their store of known facts in a spontaneous way. However, some number facts may prove more difficult for individuals, and they will need to make an effort to learn them. Learning of this kind may need to be undertaken explicitly from time to time.

An example might be the seven times table, which many children find difficult. It is worth considering how you challenge children to commit facts to memory: *'Learn the seven times table'* presents quite a daunting task, with ten facts to memorise. On the other hand, *'You know 2, 3, 4, 5 and 10 × 7. You need to learn 6, 7, 8 and 9 × 7. Since you already know half the seven times table facts, you shouldn't have too much difficulty'* is much more helpful.

Written work can develop from mental work. As was mentioned earlier, the standard algorithms we use were developed for contexts that are (in general) no longer relevant; and the National Curriculum does not specify any particular computational methods to be used. Recording mental work is a far more purposeful activity than recording calculations out of context (doing pages of already-set-out 'sums'). You may like to consider the ways in which some strategies are recorded in this book as a possible starting point for helping children to develop written methods that build on their own mental strategies.

STARTING TO USE DISCUSSION

Evidence of children's methods of working on mental maths can only be gathered through discussion. It should be noted, however, that there is a significant difference between what may be termed 'question-and-answer sessions' and true 'discussion'. Discussion is more open, and allows all participants the right to contribute. It is facilitated by the use of open (rather than closed) questions. For example, *'How many pairs of numbers can you find which multiply to give 12?'* is more challenging than *'What is 3 × 4?'* Questioning which challenges children to apply, synthesise or explain their knowledge is much more effective in raising their attainment than questioning which merely tests the ability to recall facts and procedures.

When children first start to work on developing their mental methods, they often respond to questions such as *'How did you do that?'* with *'In my head'* or *'I don't know'*. Such responses *may* mean exactly what they say; however, it is more likely that they indicate:

• disbelief at what you are asking (*'I've never been asked this before – I must have misunderstood'*);
• reluctance to tell the truth, because they

worked out the calculation in their own way (using a 'non-school' method) and they fear being told off by the teacher;
• reluctance to tell the truth because they fear (peer or teacher) ridicule (they perceive their methods to be strange and assume that others do things differently);
• a lack of appropriate vocabulary (*'I know what I did, I just can't explain it'*);
• a lack of trust or a fear of failure (*'What use is going to be made of my answer?'* or *'Am I going to get myself into something I can't get out of?'*).

Overcoming these difficulties and encouraging the children to give longer responses than the traditionally acceptable one-word (or number) answer will require patience. Modelling suitable responses, either by offering alternatives or by reflecting back what a child has said, helps pupils to develop vocabulary and a sense of what constitutes an acceptable answer. You can offer suggestions aimed at addressing the points above:

● *'Teachers don't often ask this, do they?...'*
● *'I know I would have done that one by... Is that how you solved it?'*
● *'Did you do it the same way as you would do it on paper, or did you use another way?'*
● *'You gave the right answer, I'm wondering how you worked it out.'*
● *'I think I understand what you are saying. Did you (rephrase explanation)?'*
● *'Do you think you got the right answer to this? What makes you think your answer is correct?'*

It is important to value all responses, while also encouraging children to try more efficient strategies that have been used by their peers or suggested as possible by yourself:

'Those are all good ways of working it out. Which was the quickest way? (Kim's.) Can you remember how Kim's method worked? You could try to use that method for this one...'

Each activity in this book offers specific questions to help you to draw out the children's mental maths strategies. Where appropriate, ways of introducing specific mathematical vocabulary are highlighted.

Although at all times you need to guard against turning a mental strategy into another algorithm to learn, it may be necessary to offer more efficient

strategies if they are not being developed by the children. Any strategies that you offer in this way need to be added to the range of strategies available, rather than replacing the others.

WAIT TIME

The time between asking a question and expecting a response is called the 'wait time'. Research[1] has shown that many teachers wait for less than one second before expecting a pupil to answer or moving on to someone else. A wait time of about three seconds significantly improves both the attainment and the attitude of children. But, perhaps surprisingly, waiting too long for an answer can have the effect of diminishing the quality of interaction between teacher and child and reducing the level of child achievement. Getting the wait time right is important.

When thinking about how much wait time to leave, it is important to consider the kind of question you have asked: a test of simple recall requires a shorter wait time than a more challenging question; a single-word reply takes less time to formulate than an explanation or a description.

MAKING POSITIVE USE OF INCORRECT ANSWERS

While accuracy is important, you can often learn more about a pupil's understanding by discussing incorrect answers. Often teachers avoid doing this because they do not want to discourage or worry a child. However, leaving a pupil knowing that he/she 'got it wrong' but not knowing why can foster an 'I can't do it' attitude which may be difficult to break later.

In tackling incorrect answers, a variety of possibilities need to be considered:

● *Has the question been misunderstood?*
Asked to find the missing number in 7 + ? = 15, a child may give the answer 22 through adding together the 7 and the 15. This may be due to carelessness, or it may result from the child not being able to 'read' a question where the answer is required before the '=' sign.
● *Is the solution procedure used inherently incorrect?*
Asked to solve 'Joan was given £24 for her birthday. She spent £7.50. How much does she have left?' a child may give the answer £23.50 because: 'There is 50p change, then 7 – 4 is 3 and the 20 is left.' This demonstrates significant misunderstanding. The child might go further if pressed to explain: 'Well, I knew there would be 50p because 50p and 50p is £1. Then I looked at the 7 and the 4 and I thought it would be 4 – 7, but I know you can't take a big number from a small number, so I did 7 – 4 and that was 3. And nothing happened in the tens column, so that stayed the same.'

● *Has there been an arithmetical error?*
A correct strategy has been used but an inaccuracy has crept in. Asked to solve the problem of Joan's birthday money, the following answer may be given: 'Well, if I add 50p, that's £8 and £3 makes £10 and another £14 makes £24 – so that's £17.50 left.' A prompt such as '8 and 3 is 10?' is usually enough to sort out this kind of problem.

It is clear from these examples that the work you would need to undertake in each instance would be very different. Before working with one child on a particular misconception, it is valuable to ask 'Who agrees?', 'Who else used the same method?' or 'Did anyone else get the same answer?' It is often worth offering another child the opportunity to explain why he/she thinks someone's method has not worked.

THE USE OF PRAISE

Praise is important. We praise positive behaviours to reinforce them, but to be really effective praise needs to be specific. 'Good' and 'Well done' are vague: what was good? Which bit did I do well?

'Well done, you remembered that it is quicker to count on from the largest number. That is much easier, isn't it?'

'Good, you explained that very clearly and everyone has understood you. You used all the mathematical terms correctly.'

These are specific: the child is left in no doubt as to what was done well, and the positive aspect has been reinforced.

Even where incorrect answers have been obtained, praise can be used to boost confidence: 'Well, you got the wrong answer, but the strategy was a good one and it would have worked if you hadn't made an arithmetical error.'

DISCUSSION DEVICES

Managing discussions is difficult – especially if you and your class are new to the idea. Here are some devices you might find useful to try.
● Count to five in your head before expecting an answer from the child you have asked.
● Let the children know that you are going to ask several people what they think before you all discuss their responses.
● Don't let children put their hands up – tell them you will decide who you want to ask.
● Pose a problem to be worked out by pairs. Before the children report back, give them a time warning: *'In three minutes we are going to hear what everyone has found out. You need to decide who is going to report back and what they are going to say.'*
● Encourage children to develop a clear style of explanation: *'Did everyone understand what Kay said?'*; *'Which part of what Kay said are you having difficulty with?'*; *'Kay, can you explain that a little differently? Not everyone understood you'*; *'Does anyone think they can help Kay?'*

GENERIC QUESTIONS

Many questions are generally useful in this type of discussion; some of these are listed below. They may be useful as starting points for discussion about any of the activities in this book. (In addition, each activity in this book has some specific questions suggested alongside.)

'What answer did you get?
How did you do that?
Did anyone else use that method?
Did anyone get the same answer by a different method?
Did anyone get a different answer?
How did you get that answer?'

'Any other answers or methods?'

'Do you think there is more than one correct answer for this problem?
Why do you think that?
Does anyone disagree? (Why do you disagree?)'

'Which answer do we think is correct?
Why is this answer incorrect?
Why did Sam get a wrong answer?
Can anyone help Sam see where her mistake is?
Can you see your mistake now?
How can you remember not to make a similar mistake again?'

'Which of the methods we used is the quickest? Why?
Who used that method?' (A number of hands go up.) *'Good.'*

'Who thinks they could try that method for this problem?
Who feels they would not be able to use it for this problem?
Can you explain why?
Would one of the people who used this method last time be prepared to work with Carl the next time, if he wants help?'

FOLLOW-UP

The following may be useful as ways to help the children remember strategies or number facts.
● Have a 'Fact for the day' and return to it frequently throughout the day.
● Ask individual children what mistakes they made and how they will remember not to make the same mistakes again.
● Ask other children how they might help an individual remember something.
● Ask the children to invent mnemonics for their successful strategies.

THE ACTIVITIES IN THIS BOOK

The activities in this book are organised into four chapters:
● Counting and ordering numbers.
● Addition and subtraction.
● Multiplication and division.
● Multistep and mixed operations.
Each chapter starts with examples of the kinds of strategy that need to be developed by children in Years 3 and 4/P4 and 5. All of the activities that follow can be used as a basis for whole-class or group discussions. The activities fall into four categories which require decreasing teacher input:
1 Teacher-directed activities – these are designed to be led exclusively by the teacher with a large group or the whole class. They focus explicitly on number to allow strategies to be discussed. They may also be used as general assessment activities, enabling the teacher to select appropriate follow-up work for different groups of children.
2 Problems in context – these focus on number in realistic contexts. The strategies developed in the teacher-led activities will need to be applied here. Work may be teacher-directed or undertaken collaboratively by small groups or pairs of children.
3 Investigations – these focus on number and algebra, and are designed to encourage children to generalise their findings.
4 Games – these are designed to be used independently by pairs or small groups of children. They are designed to help pupils develop their strategies in a less formal context.

REFERENCES

[1] Askew, M. and Wiliam, D. *Recent Research in Mathematics Education 5–16*, London, HMSO.

STRATEGIES

CHILDREN SHOULD BE WORKING WITH NUMBERS OF THE ORDER:

YEAR 3/PRIMARY 4

Counting

● forwards and backwards in 1s, 2s, 10s or 100s from any number;

● forwards in 5s from any number and backwards in the familiar counting chain (55, 50, 45, 40 ... 5);

● in steps of other sizes, such as 3s or 4s;

● back beyond 0;

● fractional chains with familiar fractions, eg $\frac{1}{4}$, $\frac{1}{2}$, $\frac{3}{4}$, 1, $1\frac{1}{4}$, $1\frac{1}{2}$, $1\frac{3}{4}$, 2... .

Reading and ordering

● numbers to at least 1000;

● know the values of digits in numbers to 100 000;

● read simple fractions – as above, but also including tenths and thirds;

● order a set of familiar fractions;

● order decimals in the context of money.

YEAR 4/PRIMARY 5

Counting

● forwards and backwards in whole-number (integer) steps of any size, beyond 0 if necessary;

● fractional chains including tenths (relating these to decimals).

Reading and ordering

● read, order and know the values of digits in numbers to at least 10 000;

● read and order negative numbers;

● recognise equivalence between familiar fractions (eg $\frac{6}{12} = \frac{1}{2}$, $\frac{3}{9} = \frac{1}{3}$, $\frac{25}{100} = \frac{1}{4}$);

● recognise decimals in the context of a range of measures.

Children need to become confident in reading, writing and ordering a variety of different number types at this stage. They need to develop a confident feel for the size of numbers and a sense of which numbers are appropriate to use in different situations, approximating when it is sensible to do so. They also need to be exposed to situations where estimation skills are valued, and should be encouraged to see estimation and approximation as integral aspects of the mathematical process of refining answers.

Children need to develop a clear understanding of the place value system and a sense of the power of the decimal number system to represent an infinite range of numbers in written form.

Reading numbers – at all times encourage the correct reading of numbers:

4236 is 'four thousand, two hundred and thirty-six' NOT 'four-two-three-six', and 5.75 is 'five point seven five' NOT 'five point seventy-five'.

The 'size' of a number is determined by the values of its digits. The key things for the child to know are how the value of each digit is determined by its place, the relative sizes of the different digits and the role of 0 as a place holder:

In 6303, the two 3s have different values – one is one hundred times greater than the other. The 0 is needed to 'place' the six thousand and three hundred.

This analysis also applies to decimal numbers:

In 23.03, one 3 is again one hundred times greater than the other (being two places to the left of it); again, the 0 is needed to 'place' the other numbers.

Patterns should be highlighted and discussed with the children wherever they occur. The children need to be confident about counting in groups, forwards or backwards, from any starting point. The patterns which arise from this help children to generalise rules for manipulating numbers, and can both act as a check on the count and become part of a more general 'sense' of number.

Counting on in 10s: 28 + 30 → 28, 38, 48, 58 (same unit)
Counting on in 5s: 27 + 25 → 27, 32, 37, 42, 47, 52 (alternate units)
Counting on in 2s: always even or always odd, depending on the starting number.
Counting on in 3s: always alternate odd and even numbers.

Extend the number system to give the children access to:

● Negative numbers – counting activities can all be extended 'below zero', and the number line is a key resource to help with visualising this. The fact that 'bigger' negative numbers represent smaller values should be discussed in relation to a familiar context:

A temperature of –5°C is less than –2°C.
A debt of £2 is preferable to one of £5.

● Larger numbers – children should count in thousands and see that ten thousand and one hundred thousand are written as 10 000 and 100 000 respectively.

● Decimals – these can be introduced as counting numbers (eg the numbers between 4 and 5). Again, a number line is a useful image:

5
4.9
4.8
4.7
4.6
4.5
4.4
4.3
4.2
4.1
4

Once the children are used to this idea, they can look at the numbers between 4.3 and 4.4.

● **Fractions** – mental maths activities involving fractions should emphasise fractions as real numbers as well as parts of a whole. On its own, the 'slices of cake' model often leaves children thinking that fractions cannot also be real numbers. Quite early on in fraction work, children should become comfortable relating fractions to their decimal equivalents (for halves, quarters and tenths at least).

Practical resources for counting and ordering are not only useful in Key Stage 1/ Primary 1–3. Number lines, 100 squares, base 10 blocks, abacuses and sets of arrow cards are all valuable resources for older children. Variety is important, because different resources will work better for different children. At this stage, they should aid consolidation of counting strategies, building on work in the early years. The strong working images of number that they give children can also be used as a starting point for work on mental addition and subtraction.

COUNTING AND ORDERING

MISSING NUMBERS

†† *Whole class* ⏱ *Two sessions of 20 minutes*

AIMS

To put numbers in order. To recognise patterns in a number square.

YOU WILL NEED

A board or overhead projector, squared paper (optional).

WHAT TO DO

Draw up either of the sets of diagrams (see Figure 1) on the board, or on an overhead projector transparency. (Set B is more challenging.) Tell the children that these grids are bits of a number square (1 to 100) and that the puzzle is to work out the missing numbers in each bit. As solutions are suggested, the children should be asked to explain why particular numbers go in those places. Children can follow this up by working in pairs to create similar puzzles for each other on squared paper.

DISCUSSION QUESTIONS

● *What can you say about any pair of numbers that are next to each other horizontally?*
● *What can you say about any pair of numbers that are next to each other vertically?*

EXTENSIONS

Ask the children to *imagine* a number square. Then ask them ask questions such as:
● *I'm thinking of the number 26. What number is above it/below it/to the left of it/to the right of it?*
● *I'm thinking of the number 42. What numbers are next to it? Which direction is each of these in?*
● *I'm thinking of the number 37. What number is above and to the right of it?*
● *I'm thinking of the number 45. What number is two below it? Three above it?*

Figure 1
Set A   Set B

CALL THE CARDS

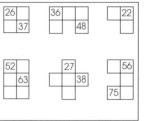

†† *Whole class, in groups of 3 and then 4*
⏱ *10–15 minutes*

AIM

To reinforce how the value of a digit depends on its place.

YOU WILL NEED

Four sets of ten A4 cards with the digits 0–9 on; space for the children to move around (the school hall would be ideal).

WHAT TO DO

Shuffle the number cards and give one to each child. Each group of three children should arrange themselves so that they form the largest possible number with their three digits. Allow a couple of minutes for this. Groups should then stand up, each member holding her/his digit, and announce the group's number. They should stand in a line so that it is clear who is 'hundreds', who is 'tens' and who is 'units'; but the number should be read as a whole, for example seven hundred and fifty three (NOT 7-5-3). After some discussion (see below), the cards should be collected, shuffled and redistributed. Repeat as before. After five or six rounds, stop for some general discussion.

Repeat the activity with groups of four children.

DISCUSSION QUESTIONS

After each round ask:
● *Which group has the largest number? The second and third largest? How can you be sure?*
● *Whose digit is worth... (eg) 60? Anyone else?*
  After several rounds:
● *How does your group decide on the order to put the digits in?*
● *When comparing your number with the others, what do you look for first? Then what?*

VARIATION

Make the smallest possible number with the three digits.

EXTENSIONS
● See 'The three-card shuffle' (page 17).
● Work in groups of five or more, making bigger and bigger numbers. What is the largest number the whole class can make?

NUMBER IN THE MIDDLE

†† *Whole class* 🕐 *20 minutes*

AIM
To develop fluency with number. To gain a feel for the size of numbers.

WHAT TO DO
Choose two numbers and ask the children for a number in between, somewhere approximately '*in the middle*' of the two. Then ask for another number in between that number and your first one. Now, when a child answers, he/she should pose the next question, using your first response as a model. This should continue until there are no whole numbers left. For example:

> Teacher: 'My numbers are 6 and 32, find me a number in between.'
> Mary: '20.'
> Teacher: 'Now find me a number in between 6 and 20.'
> Paul: '11, now find me a number in between 6 and 11.'
> Tariq: '9, now find me a number in between 6 and 9.'

How far you can continue with the line of questioning suggested below will depend on the age and experience of the children. With younger children, it could be established that there is something in between two consecutive numbers: 8½ is in between 8 and 9. With older children, this activity could be used to consider tenths explicitly as decimals: 7.5 is in between 7 and 8; 7.3 is in between 7 and 7.5.

DISCUSSION QUESTIONS
Are there any numbers in between 8 and 9?

VARIATIONS
● Ask the children to find numbers in between the first suggested number and the higher of the two original numbers.
● Use a large number line and ask children to come up and mark off their in-between number – on a number line it is clear visually that there are points in between any two whole numbers.

THE TRIPWIRE

†† *Whole class* 🕐 *20 minutes*

AIM
To develop confidence in counting in groups, forwards or backwards, from any starting point.

WHAT TO DO
Sit with the children in a circle. Explain to them that they will be counting from 10 to 50 and back, initially in 2s. Each time that they get back to 10, the *count number* increases by 1. 10 and 50 represent *tripwires* that they cannot cross. Start the count: '**10**, 12, 14... 46, 48, **50**, 48, 46... 12, **10**, 13, 16... 46, **49**, 46...'. The activity should be seen as a co-operative one, so that the 'difficult moments' (when the tripwire is being approached) are seen as an exciting challenge, not a test. Individual children should be given time to answer, and a shell or other object can be passed around with a rule that only the person holding it is allowed to speak.

Continue either until a particular count number has been reached or until you have been around the circle a fixed number of times.

DISCUSSION QUESTIONS
● *Which are the easiest numbers to count in? Why?*
● *Is it always easier to count forwards than backwards?*

VARIATIONS
● Use different tripwires, such as 15 and 51 or 21 and 66.
● Change the count number when either tripwire is reached.

EXTENSIONS
● Change the count number from 2 to 3 or 5 at random moments, or at the end of each minute (use a timer).
● Determine the count number randomly (use a dice or a spinner).

COUNTING AND ORDERING

COUNTING AND ORDERING

FIND THE NEAREST...

†† *Whole class*
⏲ *20 minutes, several times over fortnight*

AIM
To practise rounding numbers to the nearest ten or hundred.

YOU WILL NEED
Tens and units arrow cards cut from photocopiable page 62; one copy per child of photocopiable page 63.

WHAT TO DO
Explain to the children the rules for rounding up or down to the nearest ten. A good way is to demonstrate with a number line to 100 (photocopiable page 63), since the relative proximity to one ten or another is displayed visually. For the first couple of sessions each child could have an individual copy of this sheet (enlarged to A3 size) to refer to. Subsequently, the children can be asked to imagine it whenever they get stuck.

Have a set of tens and a set of units arrow cards (photocopiable page 62) shuffled into two piles. Pick one card randomly from each and hold them up. Read out the number and ask the children to say what it will be to the nearest ten. Repeat several times, asking individual children in turn to pick up two cards and announce the number.

DISCUSSION QUESTIONS
● *What does the tens digit tell you? What does the units digit tell you?*
● *What numbers do you know that will equal 60 when rounded up or down? 40? 70?*
● *What do numbers smaller than 5 come to when rounded to the nearest ten? (Zero.)*

VARIATION
Reverse the instructions, asking questions like: '*Tell me a number that is rounded **up** to 40'* or '*Tell me a number that is rounded **down** to 70.'* Children could show their answers using arrow cards.

EXTENSION
Ask children to round numbers up or down to the nearest 100, using the hundreds, tens and units arrow cards (page 62) and the 1000 number line (page 63).

MAKE A CHOICE

†† *Whole class* ⏲ *15 minutes*

AIM
To develop a feel for the size of numbers.

WHAT TO DO
Explain to the children that you will be asking some questions and that they are required to tell you *as quickly as possible*, without working it out, whether the answer would be greater than or less than 20. Write these two categories as headings on the board for reference.

Go slowly through a few obvious examples (such as 2 + 4, 17 + 19), then more rapidly through 5 + 6, 7 + 7, 12 + 15, 3 + 20, 16 + 16, 9 + 9, 11 + 11 and so on, gradually leading on to trickier examples such as 12 + 7 and 17 + 4, but avoiding ones that give exactly 20. Allow the children to call out their responses before canvassing a collective agreement and writing the question on the board under the appropriate heading. Then ask one child for an explanation, encouraging generalisations – '*the numbers are both very small'*, '*they are both nearly 20 on their own'*.

Refine the explanations through group discussion when a number of examples have been worked through; the use of the terms '*single-digit number'* and '*two-digit number'* should be encouraged.

DISCUSSION QUESTIONS
● *How can you tell if the answer is less than/greater than 20?*
● *Which questions are easy to answer? Which are more difficult?*
● *Why do two single-digit numbers never come to more than 20?*
● *Why do two two-digit numbers always come to at least 20?*

VARIATIONS
● Present the questions to the children visually (as 'flashcards') rather than orally.
● Ask the children to make up questions that fit different categories of answer.

EXTENSIONS
● Have more than two categories – for example, less than 10, between 10 and 20, more than 20.
● Include subtraction questions such as 25 – 7 and 37 – 10.

DEVELOPING MENTAL MATHS

IN THE JAR

†† *Whole class in groups of 4 or 5*
🕐 *30 minutes*

AIMS

To develop estimation skills. To explore strategies for grouping and counting.

YOU WILL NEED

For each group: a plastic jar or beaker with a lid, full of beads, buttons, small cubes, marbles or conkers (a different object for each container).

WHAT TO DO

Prepare one jar per group, as described above. The jars should be passed around and the children should discuss how many objects each jar contains. Rather than a single **estimate**, ask the children to suggest a **minimum** (at least...) and a **maximum** (not more than...). Each group should nominate a member to note down the agreed group estimates, and the jars are passed on from group to group.

When all the groups have made maximum and minimum estimates for each jar, each group should take responsibility for counting and checking the number of objects in one jar. Encourage grouping of objects, for example in 10s. Write up the total for each object for the groups to compare their estimates with.

After discussion of the results, the children can use the writing frame (photocopiable page 64) to reflect on what they have done.

DISCUSSION QUESTIONS

● *What is the smallest/largest possible number of beans in that container? Why do you think it is at least/at most that number?*
● *What is a good way to count them? What is a good way to check the count?*
● *Which objects were easier/more difficult to estimate the number of?*

VARIATION

Add in a stage where the lid is taken off the container and the objects in the top layer are counted; the children are then allowed to revise their estimates.

EXTENSION

Use the same objects (for example, small cubes) in a variety of different-sized containers, including some very large ones.

UP THE MOUNTAINS

†† *Pairs* 🕐 *20 minutes*

AIM

To order and approximate large numbers.

YOU WILL NEED

For each pair: a photocopied list of six or seven (actual) mountain heights; appropriate reference materials (see below).

WHAT TO DO

Prepare a list of six or seven mountains and their heights – you could use classroom resources related to current geographical study (atlas, geography texts, reference books, CD-ROMs) for this, or take the list in Figure 2 as a starting point. Introduce the activity by talking generally about mountains and by showing the children possible sources of the information. Mountain heights could be limited to a particular geographical region or worldwide. Children will need one copy of the list per pair. The challenge is to rewrite the list, putting the mountains in order of size (starting with the tallest). Children should then use resource materials to find other mountains to add to their list.

Figure 2

Everest (The Himalayas)	8 848m
Galdhopiggen (Norway)	2 469m
K2 (The Himalayas)	8 610m
Mont Blanc (The Alps)	4 807m
Mount Elbert (The Rockies)	4 339m
Mount Kea (Hawaii)	4 206m
Mount Kosciusko (Australia)	2 230m
Mount Robson (The Rockies)	3 954m

DISCUSSION QUESTIONS

● *How do you decide which mountain is the tallest, then the next?*
● *What do you do when the first digits are the same for two mountain heights?*

VARIATION

Give the children a similar challenge using the lengths of rivers.

EXTENSION

Ask the children to round the heights to the nearest 1000 metres. Do some mountains have the same height as each other when written this way?

1066 AND BEYOND

†† Pairs ⏲ **20 minutes**

AIM

To order large 'real' numbers.

YOU WILL NEED

Sources of historical facts (see below); a 1m strip of paper for each pair of children.

WHAT TO DO

You will need a list of historical events with dates. Use classroom resources (history texts, reference books, CD-ROMs) to make up a starter list of events and dates which could relate either to your class history topic or to generally famous occurrences. Introduce the activity by talking generally about various important historical events, and by showing the children possible sources of the information you have given them. The children's task is to create a timeline, marking these events in appropriate places. A strip of paper one metre long can be used, marked from 0 to 2 000; this can be compared to a general number line.

The children should then use the resource materials to find other events to add to their timeline. They should also be encouraged to discuss why we use the terms 'nineteenth century', 'twentieth century' and so on.

DISCUSSION QUESTIONS

● *Will that date go near the beginning/middle/end of the line? How can you tell?*
● *Which events happened in the same century? What number tells you that?*
● *Were any in the same decade? What number tells you that?*

EXTENSION

Include events that happened 'BC' and relate this to negative numbers, extending the timeline by attaching a further strip of paper before the 0.

THE BIGGEST PIECE

†† Whole class ⏲ **30 minutes**

AIM

To compare and order fractions.

YOU WILL NEED

One sheet of A4 paper per child.

WHAT TO DO

Give each child a piece of A4 paper. Demonstrate folding it in half, then half again (quarters), then half again (eighths). The children should fold and then open their pieces of paper, and you should then ask them questions involving the comparison of different fractions, in each case asking which of a pair of fractions is the larger. If the children pair up, each child can mark one of the fractions on her/his piece of paper to allow a direct visual comparison.

Compare these pairs:
● $\frac{1}{2}$ with $\frac{1}{4}$; $\frac{1}{2}$ with $\frac{1}{8}$; $\frac{1}{4}$ with $\frac{1}{8}$; $\frac{1}{2}$ with $\frac{3}{4}$;
● $\frac{3}{8}$ with $\frac{1}{2}$; $\frac{1}{4}$ with $\frac{7}{8}$; $\frac{2}{4}$ with $\frac{5}{8}$; $\frac{4}{8}$ with $\frac{3}{4}$.

Although the children are using a physical model of fractions, it is important to encourage numerical explanation of the results. If this is not forthcoming, then you should model it:

'In $\frac{2}{4}$ you can divide the numerator and denominator by 2 which gives $\frac{1}{2}$, so $\frac{2}{4}$ and $\frac{1}{2}$ are equal.'
'In $\frac{1}{2}$ you can multiply the numerator and denominator by 4 which gives $\frac{4}{8}$, so $\frac{1}{2}$ must be bigger than $\frac{3}{8}$.'

DISCUSSION QUESTIONS

● *How can you tell which is the bigger piece?*
● *Why is $\frac{1}{2}$ the same as $\frac{2}{4}$?*
● *What other fractions are the same as each other/are written in more than one way (ie are equivalent)?*

EXTENSION

Fold the paper one more time (into sixteenths), which increases the range of possible comparisons as well as the number of different pairs of equivalent fractions.

THE THREE-CARD SHUFFLE

†† *Pairs* ⏱ *20 minutes*

AIM
To reinforce how the value of a digit depends on its place.

YOU WILL NEED
For each pair: a set of 1–9 digit cards shuffled together; a set of arrow cards (see photocopiable page 62), paper and pencils.

WHAT TO DO
Ask each pair to pick three digit cards from their pack. They should now select all of the hundreds, tens and units arrow cards that the three selected digits represent. For example, if the three digit cards chosen are '6', '1' and '3', they should select the 600, 100, 300, 60, 10, 30, 6, 1 and 3 arrow cards.

Each pair should now make the largest possible number with the three digits (in this example they would need to select 600, 30 and 1, putting them together to make 631). They should make a note of this, then swap the arrow cards about until they have found the next largest number using the three digits. They should continue by swapping arrow cards around to make the 'next largest' until they get to the smallest possible (in this case 136). They should keep a written record of all the numbers they have made.

Work through one example with the children, then ask them to select three new digits and repeat the process. After three or four rounds, bring the pairs together for a general discussion.

DISCUSSION QUESTIONS
● *How can you work out which is the largest/smallest possible number?*
● *How can you tell when you've made all the possible numbers with your three digits?*
● *Is there the same number of possible numbers for any three digits? (Six different numbers are possible for any three different digits.)*
● *What would happen if two of the digits were the same? (Only three different numbers would be possible to make.)*

VARIATION
Pick the sets of three centrally and let each pair investigate the same digits at the same time; then compare solutions.

EXTENSION
● What happens if a zero is included as one of the three digits?

• Try with four digits (but no arrow cards). With four different digits 24 different numbers can be made; an interesting assessment point would be to see how systematically children record these solutions.

NUMBERS IN BLOCKS

†† *Pairs* ⏱ *Several 20-minute sessions*

AIMS
To read and record numbers correctly, using place value notation.

YOU WILL NEED
For each pair: a supply of base 10 apparatus – units, tens and hundreds ('small cubes, longs and flats').

WHAT TO DO
Ask the children to investigate the different numbers that can be modelled using a fixed number of blocks, at least one of each type. For example, with six blocks, variations would include:

> 2 hundreds, 3 tens, 1 unit; 3 hundreds, 1 ten, 2 units; 1 hundred, 1 ten, 4 units.

The children should use the blocks to model each number, and should then write down the numbers in order of size. In the first instance set the children a readily achievable goal, such as to find eight different numbers with seven blocks, rather than expecting them to find all the possibilities.

DISCUSSION QUESTIONS
● *What is the largest/smallest number you can make with six blocks? How can you be sure?*
● *How can you tell that this number is bigger (eg 321) than that one (eg 312)?*

COUNTING AND ORDERING

The children have to use a set of 1–10 number cards to find a number of fractions that are less than $\frac{1}{2}$ and a similar number greater than $\frac{1}{2}$. Give some examples of each and then set the children a target number to find – six or ten of each would be appropriate. (There are twenty possible fractions less than $\frac{1}{2}$ and an equal number greater than $\frac{1}{2}$, as well as four possible equivalents of $\frac{1}{2}$.)

DISCUSSION QUESTIONS

● *How can you tell when a fraction is less than $\frac{1}{2}$?* (The numerator is less than half the denominator.)
● *How can you tell when a fraction is greater than $\frac{1}{2}$?* (Numerator more than half denominator.)
● *Which fractions are equal to $\frac{1}{2}$? How can you tell?*
● *Can you find any other fractions that are equal to each other?*
● *What do you notice about all the fractions that have '1' as the numerator?* (They are all less than or equal to $\frac{1}{2}$.) *Can you put these fractions in order of size?*

VARIATION

Use a smaller range of cards, such as from 1 to 8.

EXTENSIONS

● Partners can take it in turns to make a fraction and challenge the other to make a fraction that is greater or smaller.
● Children can use the writing frame (photocopiable page 64) to reflect on their strategies for comparing fractions.

VARIATIONS

Use a spike abacus instead of base 10 equipment. Each number must now be made using the same number of beads.

EXTENSIONS

● Include thousands (large cubes).
● Ask the children to find all the possible numbers using a given number of blocks.

FIND THE FRACTIONS

†† *Pairs* ⏱ *20 minutes*

AIM

To practise judging the relative sizes of numerical fractions.

YOU WILL NEED

For each pair: a set of 1–10 number cards; a lolly stick (or similar).

WHAT TO DO

Using two number cards and a lolly stick, demonstrate how the cards can be placed above and below the horizontally placed stick to record a fraction. Explain to the children that they will be investigating **proper** fractions – that is, fractions that are less than a whole, so that the top number must be less than the bottom number. This would be a good opportunity to introduce or encourage the use of the mathematical terms '**numerator**' and '**denominator**'.

THE GREAT COVER-UP

†† Small groups ⏱ 30 minutes

AIM
To recognise patterns in the order of numbers.

YOU WILL NEED
For each group: several different number grids such as a 100 square, a 'Snakes and ladders' type of game board (photocopiable page 60) or pages from a calendar; 10 or so counters or cubes big enough to cover the numbers on the grids.

WHAT TO DO
One child (the 'coverer') selects a grid and places ten counters or cubes to cover up ten of the numbers. The rest of the group should write down what numbers they think are covered up. When they have completed this, the first child reveals the hidden numbers one at a time and the other children check their answers, scoring one point for each correct answer.

Another child now takes on the role of the 'coverer', selecting a different grid and proceeding as before. The game continues until all the children have had a chance to take on this role. Total scores can be calculated to determine the overall winner.

DISCUSSION QUESTIONS
● *How can you tell which numbers are hidden?*
● *Which grids are the easiest/hardest to work out numbers on?*

EXTENSIONS
● Let the children use squared paper to create a variety of number grids for others to use. These can reflect any aspect of number that children are currently working on.

For example, grids could show:
* Even numbers (2, 4, 6...)
* Odd numbers (1, 3, 5...)
* Fives (5, 10, 15...)
* Tens (10, 20, 30...)
* Tenths (0.1, 0.2, 0.3...)
* Negative numbers (–50, –49, –48...)

The grid dimensions can be varied, and different grids can also be created by ordering the numbers in vertical columns (rather than the normal horizontal rows) or 'there and back' in rows from the bottom up (as in a 'Snakes and ladders' board).
● The computer game 'Monty' is similar to this activity, but more challenging. It is available on the *SLIMWAMZ* software for BBC, Archimedes or RML Nimbus machines (available from ATM, 7 Shaftesbury Road, Derby DE23 8YB).

MATCH THE CARDS

†† Pairs ⏱ 15 minutes

AIM
To order and match vulgar and decimal fractions.

YOU WILL NEED
For each pair: a metre stick and a set of eighteen cards, nine marked in tenths from 0.1 to 0.9, nine marked with the vulgar fraction equivalents (depending on the children's previous experience of equivalent fractions, these can be written either all in tenths or with each fraction in its lowest terms).

WHAT TO DO
The cards should be shuffled, then drawn one at a time by each player in turn. They should be placed at the appropriate point on the metre stick; any player whose draw makes a matching pair gets to keep those two cards. The winner is the player with the most cards when they have all been paired.

DISCUSSION QUESTIONS
● *How do you know where, for example, 0.3 goes?*
● *How do you know that this decimal is the same as that fraction? Which ones are easy to pair up? Which ones are trickier?*

EXTENSIONS
● Use a long strip of paper marked '0' and '1' at the ends. The cards have to be put in order without the ruler markings as a guide. If someone neglects to leave an appropriate gap (putting 0.3 next to $\frac{1}{2}$ for example), they miss a turn. In order to get a sense of their relative positions, children could practice sorting decimal and vulgar fractions into order separately before playing this game.
● Include these further pairs: 0.25 and $\frac{1}{4}$; 0.75 and $\frac{3}{4}$; 0.33 and $\frac{1}{3}$; 0.67 and $\frac{2}{3}$.
● Children could use the writing frame on photocopiable page 64 to reflect on this activity.

STRATEGIES

CHILDREN SHOULD BE WORKING WITH NUMBERS OF THE ORDER:

YEAR 3/PRIMARY 4

● add a one-digit number to a two-digit number – bridging through ten as necessary;

● add two two-digit numbers with a total less than 50 without bridging through ten (eg 23 + 25 but not 13 +18);

● subtract a single-digit number from a two-digit number without breaking a ten (eg 27 – 4 but not 27 – 9);

● add or subtract 10 or 100 to/from a two- or three-digit number;

● add two multiples of 10 or find the difference between them.

YEAR 4/PRIMARY 5

● add any one-digit number to a two- or three-digit number;

● add two two-digit numbers with a total less than 50;

● subtract any one-digit number from a two-digit number;

● add or subtract 100 or 1000 to/from a three- or four-digit number;

● add or subtract a multiple of 10 to/from a two- or three-digit number.

AS A MINIMUM, BY THE END OF YEAR 4/PRIMARY 5 MOST CHILDREN SHOULD:

● know and use addition facts to 20;

● know and use doubles and halves of all numbers to 20;

● know and use simple fractions;

● recognise the equivalence of coins (eg 2 × 50p = £1, 20 × 5p = £1);

● recognise decimals in the context of money, measures and calculator displays.

At the beginning of this stage (Y3/P4), it is important to consolidate children's knowledge of, and confidence with, the basic addition and subtraction facts – number pairs to 20, single-digit subtraction and so on – since these are important building blocks. Many things can slow children down and stop them developing more efficient and effective methods. The single most significant problem is a lack of known number facts to draw upon. Children also need to consolidate their understanding of the relationship between the two operations. These basic aspects should be worked on in contexts which enable children to extend and apply them. Children need to rehearse their knowledge in a variety of situations that will strengthen their conceptual grasp, and also enable them to develop flexible and comfortable methods for working with larger numbers.

There is, of course, a thin line between allowing children to develop their own methods and teaching them strategies that we know work well. The following are methods that experience shows are linked to efficient mental calculation; but it is vital that children arrive at these (or similar methods) by discussion and negotiation, not by instruction (as traditional paper and pencil algorithms were once taught). Personal ownership of the method will make the children positive about themselves as mathematicians and also enable them to develop a sense of 'choosing the right method for the right occasion'.

Language: As children work on a variety of addition and subtraction problems, we need to help them make links between the language and the underlying mathematical structures. Important vocabulary includes: increase, total, sum of, more than, less than, decrease, reduce, difference between, minus.

STRATEGIES FOR ADDITION

Putting the larger number first when counting on or adding:

$3 + 12 \rightarrow 12 + 3$

Partitioning problems by splitting the numbers into their constituent parts and regrouping:

$24 + 13 \rightarrow 20 + 4 + 10 + 3$
$\rightarrow 20 + 10 + 3 + 4$
$= 30 + 7 = 37$

STRATEGIES FOR SUBTRACTION

Partitioning numbers:

$23 - 5 \rightarrow 20 - 5 + 3 = 15 + 3 = 18$

Complementary addition – this strategy is sometimes called 'Shopkeeper's addition', as it corresponds to the way in which change is often counted out. It involves deciding what has to be added to the smaller number to get to the larger:

$31 - 18 \rightarrow$ 'What do I have to add to 18 to get to 31?'
$18 + 2 = 20, 20 + 10 = 30, 30 + 1 = 31$
and $2 + 10 + 1 = 13$, so $31 - 18 = 13$

Compensation – for example, solving 'subtract 9' as '−10 + 1':

$28 - 9 = 28 - 10 + 1 = 19$

Using other known number facts such as recognising inverses:

$20 - 3 = 17$ since $17 + 3 = 20$

Bridging through 10 using familiar number bonds to 10:

$18 + 6 = 18 + 2 + 4 = 24$

Bridging strategies can be extended to deal with two two-digit numbers:

$38 + 26 \qquad = 38 + 20 + 2 + 4$
$= 58 + 2 + 4$
$= 60 + 4 = 64$

Counting on (in 10s):

$23 + 40$ as $23, 33, 43, 53, 63$

Compensation – for example, adding by using '+ 10 − 1':

$43 + 9 = 43 + 10 - 1 = 53 - 1 = 52$

Later, this might be extended to adding 19 by using '+ 20 − 1', and adding 8 by using '+ 10 − 2'.

Regrouping numbers by looking for bonds of 10:

$6 + 3 + 2 + 7 + 4 \rightarrow (6 + 4) + (3 + 7) + 2$
$= 10 + 10 + 2 = 22$

Using other known number facts such as doubles:

since $4 + 4 = 8, 40 + 40 = 80$
since double 7 is 14, $7 + 8 = 7 + 7 + 1 = 15$

DEVELOPING MENTAL MATHS

ADDITION AND SUBTRACTION

MAKE THE NUMBER

†† *Whole class* ⏰ *20 minutes*

AIM
To explore patterns in addition bonds.

WHAT TO DO
Ask the children for a number between 15 and 20 (or 20 and 25, or 25 and 30). Now ask them to think of two numbers that they can add together to make that number. When one suggestion has been made and agreed on, ask for further possible answers. If children are struggling, suggest one of a possible pair of numbers and ask what the other must be. Thus if 23 is the target, ask: *'One of my numbers is 14, what must the other be?'*

After several answers have been given, ask for a different number to work with and repeat as before. Then stop for reflection, using one of the discussion questions below.

DISCUSSION QUESTIONS
● *How do you choose your two numbers?*
● *If one number is 1 (or 2, or 10), how can you find the other easily?*
● *Which sums are more difficult to check?*
● *If 16 and 7 make 23, what must I add to 15 to get 23? Why does this work?*
● *How many different pairs of numbers make 23? How can you be sure you have found them all?*

VARIATION
Let one or two children use calculators to check the answers.

EXTENSIONS
● Have larger target numbers and introduce various restrictions, for example that both numbers must be greater than 10.
● Include simple fractions: halves to begin with, then quarters.

CARD CHANGES

†† *Whole class, in pairs*
⏰ *20 minutes, several times over a fortnight*

AIM
To develop strategies for addition and subtraction of units, tens and hundreds.

YOU WILL NEED
For each pair: a set of arrow cards (photocopiable page 62).

WHAT TO DO
Ask each pair of children to select the 600, 40 and 5 arrow cards, putting them together to make 645. Now ask them to make a series of changes to the number. Each time, one child changes the cards while the other agrees the result, then you check with the whole group before going on to give the next instruction.

The changes can be in any order; but to start with, avoid any need for exchange between hundreds and tens or between tens and units. For example, starting with 645:

Add 10 to your number.
Now add 1.
Now take away 100.
Now add 10.
Now take away 2.
Now add 200.
Now add 11.
Now take away 101.
Now add 220...
After about eight changes, stop for discussion.

DISCUSSION QUESTION

How do you... add 10? take away 100?

VARIATIONS

● Vary the language used. For addition: *'Change your number so that it is 10 more'; 'Increase your number by 200.'* For subtraction: *'Change your number so that it is 20 less'; 'Reduce your number by 100.'*

● This activity can also be done on an HTU spike abacus or using base 10 blocks.

EXTENSIONS

Increase the range of numbers so that adding or subtracting affects adjoining columns. For example:

'You have reached 798. What happens if 10 is added? Or 3?'

'You have reached 611. What happens if 20 is subtracted?'

TRUE OR FALSE?

†† *Whole class*
🕐 *20 minutes, several times over a week or fortnight*

AIM

To encourage strategies for checking.

YOU WILL NEED

Strips of card with number sentences written on; blank strips of card.

WHAT TO DO

Prepare several card strips with one number sentence clearly written on each, either addition or subtraction (or a mixture). They should be chosen to provide appropriate challenges reflecting key mental strategies (see page 20) that the children are working on. Larger numbers for which written algorithms or calculators would be more appropriate should be avoided.

Some sentences should be correct and some wrong. For example:

$$12 + 15 = 27, \quad 56 - 16 = 40, \quad 27 + 6 = 34,$$
$$32 - 15 = 27$$

Hold up each card in turn and challenge the children to tell you whether the number sentence is true or false. After a few moments, ask for someone to explain *why* it is true or false. Then ask whether anyone can explain it another way. When you feel that everyone is sure of the explanation, move on to the next question.

In subsequent sessions, the children can be given a blank card strip to set their own 'true or false' challenges.

DISCUSSION QUESTIONS

● *Is this number sentence true or false? How do you know?*
● *How do you check the answer? Is there another way to make sure?*
● *What would the correct answer be?*

VARIATION

Once the children are familiar with the format, it can be played as a small-group game.

EXTENSIONS

● Include number sentences with the answer first, eg $35 = 29 + 6$ (True).
● Include number sentences with the answer unresolved, eg $24 - 6 = 23 - 7$ (False).

TRIANGULATION

†† *Whole class*
🕐 *20 minutes, several times over a fortnight*

AIMS

To practise addition skills through regrouping. To explore the triple bonds of single-digit and two-digit totals.

WHAT TO DO

This activity involves children using the image of a triangle to rehearse various recomposing skills (see 'Strategies', page 21). In the first instance this activity can be introduced practically, with a large card triangle on which the starting number is written boldly in the centre. Choose a number that the children will feel comfortable with (see page 20); for Year 3/P4, this could be a number small enough to be modelled with cubes or counters. Children should suggest numbers to put in the corners of the triangle such that the three 'corner numbers' add up to the number in the centre.

ADDITION AND SUBTRACTION

Subsequently, begin sessions with '*I want you to imagine a triangle with the number ... at the centre. What numbers might be at the corners?*' Children's suggestions should be written up clearly on the board (as in Figure 1), so that it becomes clear that for any starting number there is a range of possibilities.

As the children become confident with this format, select variations and extensions (see below) to address specific aspects of mental calculation.

Figure 1

DISCUSSION QUESTIONS

● *How do you decide what to put on the first corner? What does that leave for the other corners?*
● *What centre numbers give the biggest number of different solutions? (See 'Three-way split', page 31.)*
● *What is special about the centre numbers that can produce three equal whole numbers at each of the corners? (They are multiples of 3.)*

VARIATIONS

● What if two of your three numbers had to be the same? (Suggest taking the unit as one of the numbers and halving the tens to find the other two.)
● What if one of the three corner numbers was 11 or 9? (Rehearse compensation strategies to find the number left to divide between the remaining two corners.)
● Choose a number that can be divided exactly by 3, such as 24 – when 8-8-8 has been suggested, ask what happens if one of the eights stays in place and one of the others is increased by 1, 2 or 3.
● Rework the activities using a rectangle, breaking the starting number into four parts.

EXTENSIONS

● What happens if $\frac{1}{2}$ is allowed? Or $\frac{1}{3}$?
● What happens if one of the three numbers is less than 0?
● Begin with an operation – for example, with the sum '15 + 16' in the centre, what numbers could go on the corners?

THIS WAY AND THAT

†† *Whole class* 🕐 *20 minutes*

AIMS

To develop strategies for adding or subtracting 9.

YOU WILL NEED

For each child: a 100 square and two counters or other markers. You will also need one dice or spinner marked + 10, + 10, + 9, – 10, – 9, – 9.

WHAT TO DO

Each child should put one counter somewhere in the middle of her/his 100 square. Throw the dice and announce the number and operation. The children should add/subtract the number and put a second counter on the new position. After checking that everyone has the second counter in the right place, throw the dice again. The children should add/subtract this number to/from the second position and move the original counter to show the result.

Continue for a half a dozen or so throws, with the children moving the counters alternately, before stopping for discussion. Try to steer the discussion towards compensation strategies, if the children do not identify these for themselves. (See page 21.) Once the children are confidently explaining what is happening (see below), continue with one of the extension activities.

DISCUSSION QUESTIONS

● *What happens to the counters when you add or subtract 10? Why is this?*
● *Look at the two counters when you have added or subtracted 9. What do you notice about their positions? How did you decide where to put the second counter?*

VARIATIONS

● Use a large 100 square (an overhead projector transparency is ideal), and after the dice is thrown ask the children to suggest where you should put the new counter.
● Try the same activity using a 100 number line.

EXTENSIONS

● Use alternative dice/spinners with these sets of numbers:

+ 11, + 10, + 9, – 11, – 10, – 9
+ 11, + 9, + 9, – 11, – 11, – 9
+ 10, + 9, + 8, – 10, – 9, – 8
+ 12, + 10, + 8, – 12, – 10, – 8

● The children could use the writing frame on photocopiable page 64 to reflect on this activity.

MORE OR LESS

🏃 *Whole class* 🕐 *20 minutes*

AIM

To reinforce compensation strategies for adding or subtracting 9.

WHAT TO DO

This activity follows directly from the previous one. Here, the numbers are dealt with more abstractly and the compensation strategies are brought in more explicitly.

Ask someone to choose a number between 20 and 80. Now ask questions such as:
● *'What happens if you add 9/10/11 to it?'*
● *'What happens if you subtract 9/10/11 from it?'*

When the children are answering confidently, vary the vocabulary used:
● *'I'm thinking of 43, what happens if I **increase/reduce** it by 9/10/11?'*
● *'What number is 9/10/11 **more than/less than** 74?'*

DISCUSSION QUESTIONS

● *How can you quickly add 9/10/11 to any number?*
● *How can you quickly subtract 9/10/11 from any number?*
(See page 21.)

EXTENSIONS

● Include the addition/subtraction of 8 and 12, using the same principle.
● Include the addition/subtraction of 19, 29... and 18, 28... , using the same principle.

RETURN TO NUMBER 10

🏃 *Whole class* 🕐 *20 minutes*

AIM

To practise mental addition where bridging through a ten is required.

WHAT TO DO

Start by asking the children to add numbers on to 10. Choose two numbers for them to add on: first a two-digit number such as 18 or 27, then a second number such that bridging through a ten is required – for Year 3/Primary 4 children this could be a single-digit number and for more confident/older children a two-digit number. Repeat this several times, always starting at 10. Each time, ask the children to say number sentences. There should then be explicit discussion of the different strategies used for the different types of addition sums.

Now challenge the children to *'Return to number 10'*, using two different numbers from those previously added to the 10. They should try to find 'easy ways' to do this; for example, to get back from 35 to 10, subtract 5 and then 20.

DISCUSSION QUESTIONS

● *How do you add the number to 10? Is there an easy way to do it?*
● *How do you add 6 to 38? Does everyone do it that way?*
(If no one suggests splitting the 6 into 2 and 4, offer it yourself as a quick way.)
● *We are at 44, what would be an easy way to get back to 10?*
(If no one suggests subtracting 4 and then subtracting 30, suggest it yourself and ask what makes it an 'easy' solution.)

VARIATIONS

● Use different starting numbers, for example, 20 or 30.
● Allow different numbers of steps to get back to the starting number.

EXTENSION

Start at 80 or 90 and go above 100.

ADD THIS, TAKE THAT

†† *Whole class*
🕐 *20 minutes, several times over a fortnight*

AIM

To develop bridging and compensation strategies for addition and subtraction of single-digit numbers.

WHAT TO DO

Arrange the class in a circle. The children count around the circle, commencing from 0, alternately adding and subtracting. Work around slowly, as in the counting activity 'The tripwire' (page 13), allowing each child time to answer. (A shell or other object can be passed around, and only the holder allowed to answer.)

Write up the counting rule where all can refer to it. The simplest rule is 'ADD 2, TAKE 1'. This count will proceed 0, 2, 1, 3, 2, 4, 3, 5... It is a good idea to have a definite end point, for example twice around the circle or when 100 is reached. Once the format is familiar, the number range can easily be extended. Try 'ADD 5, TAKE 2', 'ADD 5, TAKE 3', 'ADD 4, TAKE 2' or 'ADD 10, TAKE 9'. After each round, encourage reflection on the different strategies the children have employed or any patterns they may have noticed. After trying with several different rules, the children should reflect on any similarities and differences they may have noticed. (Note that at this stage, the 'add' number should always be larger than the 'take' number.)

DISCUSSION QUESTIONS

● *Which numbers are easy to add/take away? Which are more difficult?*
● *Are there other ways of working out your answers?*
● *Which rules make the numbers bigger quickest?*

VARIATIONS

● Begin at 20 or 30 – the children will reach less familiar numbers more quickly.
● The children can play in a group, marking their progress on a 0–100 number line (photocopiable page 63, enlarged to A3) or keeping track on a calculator.

EXTENSIONS

● Begin at 50 or 100 and have a rule such as 'ADD 1, TAKE 2', where the 'add' number is smaller than the 'take' number; this will lead naturally into negative numbers.
● Begin at a negative number, for example –20 with the rule 'ADD 3, TAKE 2'.
● Try with larger numbers: 'ADD 100, TAKE 50' or 'ADD 50, TAKE 30'. The children can use the 0–1000 number line (photocopiable page 63, enlarged to A3) to mark their progress.

FIND THE BALANCE

†† *Whole class or groups* ⏲ *30 minutes*

AIM

To practise regrouping strategies for addition.

YOU WILL NEED

A pan balance with 1g, 2g, 5g, 10g and 20g weights; a board.

Figure 2

WHAT TO DO

Use some weights (see above) to demonstrate how a pan balance works. For example, put a 10 gram and a 50 gram weight in one side and three 20 gram weights on the other side. (See Figure 2.) Write the corresponding sums up on the board: 10 + 50 = 20 + 20 + 20. Discuss the meaning of the equals sign in this context: it tells you that there is a balance between the two sides. Ask the children to suggest how the smaller weights could be combined to make the larger ones – for example, two 20g weights and one 10g weight make 50g.

Now pose further questions, insisting that there must be a **minimum of two** weights on either side:

> 'If there are a 50g and a 20g on the left, what could be on the right?'
>
> 'If there are two 20g and a 5g on the left, what could be on the right?'

DISCUSSION QUESTIONS

● *Can you explain how your weights will make it balance? Is there another possible answer?*
● *What different ways can you make 50g using smaller weights?*
(You could remind the children of similar activities using coins to make up a given value such as 50p.)

EXTENSION

Use irregular weights: 23g, 17g and so on. These could be made as actual weights by gluing together smaller plastic weights (which would be a good mathematical exercise for the children), or they can be tokens.

THE STRANGE SWEETSHOP

†† *Class, then pairs* ⏲ *30 minutes*

AIMS

To practise addition skills with money. To explore number bonds for addition. To develop systematic investigation.

YOU WILL NEED

Photocopiable page 64 (optional). Some coins of all the denominations up to £1 (see below) would be useful.

WHAT TO DO

Ask the children to recall the different coin denominations under £1: 1p, 2p, 5p, 10p, 20p, 50p. Tell them about a strange sweetshop where the shopkeeper refuses to give change, but where you will only ever need to use two coins to buy something. The cost of an item might, for instance, be 7p (5p and 2p) or 40p (20p and 20p). Using one coin is not allowed.

Let the children work in pairs to find possible prices for items. There are in fact 21 different possibilities, but it is a good idea is to suggest a minimum number for each pair to find. The results can be pooled to help determine the full range of answers.

After discussion, the children could use the writing frame (photocopiable page 64) to reflect on their strategies.

DISCUSSION QUESTIONS

● *How many prices do you think there are?*
● *Which pairs of coins are easy to add? Is there a way to check your answer?*
● *How can we work systematically to make sure we have found all the possible combinations?*

VARIATION

Only allow one of each coin – no duplicates. (There will then be only 15 possibilities.)

ADDITION AND SUBTRACTION

ADDITION AND SUBTRACTION

EXTENSIONS

● Include £1 coins; any two coins can be used for a purchase. (There are 28 possibilities with duplicates and 21 without.)
● In the shop next door, each item can be purchased with three coins. £1 coins are excluded. (There are 56 possibilities with duplicates and 20 without.)

DARTBOARD 1

†† *Whole class, working in pairs*
🕐 *20 minutes, several times over a fortnight*

AIM

To develop strategies for regrouping and combining numbers.

YOU WILL NEED

A board or overhead projector; photocopiable page 61.

WHAT TO DO

Introduce this activity by discussing the scoring system in darts: there is a single, double and treble region for each number, and players try to reach their target total by combining

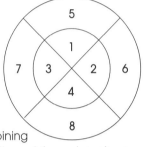

dart scores. Draw the dartboard (see above) up on the board, or make up an overhead projector transparency using the blank on photocopiable page 61. Ask the children to work in pairs, finding different ways to make 15 with three darts. They may use the same number more than once, but all darts must score. The emphasis should be on speed, so after a couple of minutes stop and pool the results to see if all the possible solutions have been found. Repeat for other totals.

Once the children are familiar with the 'dartboard' model, use the blank version on page 61 to create alternative number sets based on the range of numbers that you want the class to work with; different pairs can work with different number sets, aiming at different targets. Children can use three counters or cubes to mark their numbers in each turn.

Some possible dartboards are:
● Numbers 2 to 5 (put two of each on the grid).
● Numbers 6 to 9 (put two of each on the grid).
● Numbers 3 to 10.
● All even numbers, 2 to 16 (target must be even).
● All odd numbers, 1 to 15 (target must be odd).
● Numbers from 7 to 13.
● Multiples of 5: 5 to 40 (target a multiple of 5).
● Multiples of 10: 10 to 80 (target a multiple of 10).
● Include negative numbers: –4, –3, –2, –1, 1, 2, 3, 4.

DISCUSSION QUESTIONS

● *How did you add the numbers? How did you check your result?*
● *If 1/2/3/4/5 is the first score, what does that leave for the other two darts?*
● *If you had two twos/threes/fours/fives/sixes/ sevens, what would that leave for the third dart?*
● *If the target is 15, why can't you have two darts scoring 8 each?*
● *What ways have you used to find or check your answers?*

VARIATIONS

● Play with only two darts.
● Allow darts to 'miss', effectively counting 0 as one of the possible scores.
● All three darts must score a different number.
● Play with four darts.
Also see the multistep activity 'Dartboard 2' on page 54.

EXTENSION

Ask the children to investigate the following problem: *You have three darts. Find at least one way to achieve each score between 3 (the minimum with each dart scoring) and 24 (the maximum). Which scores can be made up in the greatest number of ways?* (Those in the middle of the range.)

FROG HOPS

†† *Individual work* 🕐 *20 minutes*

AIM

To explore patterns in addition.

YOU WILL NEED

For each child: some paper, a pencil, a counter (to represent the frog).

WHAT TO DO

Tell the children that the frog is able to jump across a 20m field in three hops, with each hop an exact number of metres up to a maximum of 10m. Each child should then draw a picture to show what the frog has done, making it clear where the frog was after each 'hop'.

The children should realise that many different 'hopping patterns' are possible. They can be given a target number of solutions – say four or five. When they have found these, they should be given a different length to cross, such as 17m or 27m. (Keep to a maximum of 30m.)

DISCUSSION QUESTIONS
● *How do you choose your three numbers?*
● *If the first jump was very small, say only 1 metre, what would the other two jumps be like?*
● *If the first hop is 10 metres, how far does the frog have left to jump?*

VARIATION
Keep the total length the same, but vary the number of frog hops.

EXTENSION
Allow half-metre jumps, so that (for example) 20m could be made up of 6.5m, 8m and 5.5m jumps.

LESS THAN £1

†† *Whole class* ⏲ *20 minutes*

AIMS
To explore ways of finding complements of 100. To practise the 'shopkeeper's addition' strategy for subtraction.

YOU WILL NEED
Several items: a pen, a pencil, scissors, small toys, small grocery items and so on. Label each item with a cost less than £1.

WHAT TO DO
Ask a child to choose one of the items and read out the cost; then ask all the children to work out how much change they would get from £1 if they bought it. Ask them to explain this the way that a shopkeeper might – if children are unsure of this, then model the shopkeeper:

The exercise book cost 58p, so here's 2p, that's 60p, and 20p and another 20p makes £1. So that's 42p change altogether.

With younger or less confident children, you might prefer to start with items priced in multiples of 10p, then go on to items priced in multiples of 5p, then lead on to a full range of costs, below £1.

DISCUSSION QUESTIONS
● *How did you work out the change? Is there another way to check?*
● *If something costs 'forty-something' pence, how much change will you get?*
(This encourages generalisation.)

VARIATIONS
● Model the questions on a 0–100 number line, encouraging the children to visualise complements.
● Use base 10 blocks or Cuisenaire rods to model the questions.

EXTENSIONS
● Buy any **two** items (all the single-item costs should be less than 50p) and work out the change from £1.
● The children can use the writing frame on photocopiable page 64 to reflect on their strategies.

ADD OR SUBTRACT?

†† *Whole class, groups* ⏲ *30 minutes*

AIM
To interpret word problems in terms of addition and subtraction.

WHAT TO DO
Give the children some examples of word problems that require addition or subtraction, such as:

A bar of chocolate costs 26p. If the price increases by 3p, how much will it cost?
Kelly had 23 swap cards but lost 4. How many does he now have?

Ask the children whether they need to do an addition or a subtraction to find the answer. Spend some time discussing how they know which operation is needed before they actually perform the operation. They should then check by using the reverse operation.

Discuss the various addition and subtraction terms including *more than, increase, total, decrease, less than* and *difference*. Ask the

children to use one of these expressions to make up some word problems. They should then try these out in groups, always asking whether each problem requires an addition or subtraction before calculating, then checking their answers. When they are satisfied with these problems, they could write out neat copies to collect together for a class book or display.

It would be useful to raise here (if it hasn't already been covered) the issue of questions which take the form 'What is the difference between...?' Such questions require a subtraction, but a common strategy for finding the answer is complementary addition or 'shopkeeper's addition'. (See page 21.) For example:

> 'What is the difference between 26 and 19? can be solved as $26 - 19 = 16 - 9 = 7$ or can be solved by making 19 up to 26, adding first 1 (to make 20) and then 6 (to make 26). Therefore the difference is $1 + 6 = 7$.

DISCUSSION QUESTIONS

● *How did you solve the problem? How can you check your solution?*
● *Is all the information there that you need? Is there anything extra there that you don't need?*

VARIATION

Give the children number sentences (in numerical form) to create word problems from – this way, you can limit the range of questions to numbers the children are confident with, or you can focus on particular strategies (such as adding/subtracting 9).

THE MILOMETER

†† *Whole class, then pairs*   🕐 *30 minutes*

AIM

To develop addition with larger numbers, bridging tens and hundreds.

YOU WILL NEED

A board; squared paper.

WHAT TO DO

Ask the children if they have ever watched the milometer in a car. This device shows how many miles a car has gone. Discuss how it works: it is like a digital abacus. For example, if it is showing '04759', one more mile returns the unit figure to '0' and increases the tens figure to '6'. Draw up the following diagram to record what has happened:

| 0 | 4 | 7 | 5 | 9 | → 1 mile | 0 | 4 | 7 | 6 | 0 |

Ask the children what will happen if the milometer shows '04759' miles and the car then does a journey of 2, 3, 5 or 10 miles. They should state the new mileage as a real number: *'four thousand, seven hundred and sixty'*, not *'four seven six nought'*.

Now consider a milometer showing '06299'. What happens when the car makes a journey of 2, 3, 5 or 10 miles?

| 0 | 6 | 2 | 9 | 9 | → | | | | | |

After some discussion, the children can work in pairs to pose and solve their own milometer problems. A grid to record these can be made up on squared paper.

DISCUSSION QUESTIONS

● *What is a good way to add on the number? How can you check your result?*
● *What is the biggest number that can be shown on the dial?*

EXTENSION

Let the children add on to numbers ending in '999' and '9999' (or '98', '998' and '9998'), using a similar model.

THREE-WAY SPLIT

†† *Groups of 3* ⏱ *20–30 minutes*

AIMS

To investigate triple bonds of a given total. To develop addition skills through regrouping.

YOU WILL NEED

Photocopiable sheet 64 (optional).

WHAT TO DO

This investigation stands on its own, but could also be undertaken as a development of the activity 'Triangulation' (see page 23). In groups, the children will work on triangles as in the previous activity; but this time, they are trying to find *all* the possible combinations that will give a particular total. Different groups can be given different target numbers, and particular restrictions can be set in order to provide a variety of challenges:

● No 0s allowed.
● No numbers below 5 (target must be greater than 15, try 25 or 32).
● No numbers above 10 (target must be less than 30, try 19 or 22).
● All three numbers must be odd (target must be an odd number, try 25 or 31).
● All three numbers must be even (target must be an even number, try 30 or 40).
● No two numbers can be the same.
● Two of the three numbers must be the same.

One possible way for the groups of three to work would be for them to take turns to suggest the first of the three numbers, leaving the other two to decide together on the remaining two numbers – each of the three then records one of the corners.

Following discussion, the children can use the writing frame on photocopiable page 64 to reflect on their strategies.

DISCUSSION QUESTIONS

● *How do you choose each of your three numbers?*
● *How many different solutions might be possible? How can you be sure you have found them all?*

EXTENSIONS

● Include at least one negative number in the solutions.
● Use other shapes: squares, pentagons or hexagons.

TOTALIZER

†† *Pairs* ⏱ *20–30 minutes*

AIM

To practise addition strategies.

YOU WILL NEED

For each pair: a set of 0–9 number cards; paper and pencils; a copy of the recording grid (optional).

WHAT TO DO

Write up the recording grid shown in Figure 3 (see page 32) on the board, or provide a photocopied version for each pair. Working together, the children should pick four cards at random; the challenge is to arrange the four numbers to form the largest total for each of the four different digit arrangements on the grid. They should then repeat this for other sets of four numbers, using a new copy of the grid each time.

DISCUSSION QUESTIONS

● *How do you check each of the additions?*
● *How can you be sure you've found the largest total for each arrangement?*
● *Which of the four arrangements gives the largest total of all? Would that happen for any four numbers you chose?*

VARIATIONS

● For a simpler version, use only three digits (and a modified grid). The possible arrangements of the digits will be two-digit plus single-digit or three single digits.
● Challenge the children to find the smallest possible totals in each case.

EXTENSION

Start with five digits (and a modified grid).

There are six possible arrangements of these digits on the grid: five single-digit numbers; one two-digit and three single-digit numbers; one three-digit and two single-digit numbers; one four-digit and one single-digit number; one three-digit and one two-digit number; two two-digit and one single-digit numbers.

Figure 3

Our four numbers are:
These sums give the largest totals:

☐ + ☐ + ☐ + ☐ =

☐☐ + ☐ + ☐ =

☐ + ☐☐ =

☐☐ + ☐ =

WALK THE LINE

†† *Pairs* ⏲ *30 minutes*

AIM
To add tens, bridging through 100.

YOU WILL NEED
For each pair: A vertical number line marked in tens from 0 to 200 (see left); two dice (or spinners) – one marked 40, 50, 60, 70, 80, 100 and the other marked 0, 20, 30, 50, 70, 90; small round labels to cover the numbers on the dice; a marker pen.

200 —
190 —
180 —
170 —
160 —
150 —
140 —
130 —
120 —
110 —
100 —
90 —
80 —
70 —
60 —
50 —
40 —
30 —
20 —
10 —
0 —

WHAT TO DO
The dice are thrown and the numbers added together. The total is marked off on the number line. After ten or twelve throws, the children look at the totals on the line that have NOT come up. For each of these, they should decide whether it was possible or impossible for that total to have come up given the numbers on the dice. They should then change the numbers on the dice (by covering the current numbers with labels and marking on new values) to make it possible for the 'impossible' totals to be arrived at by adding two dice scores. (Other totals may, of course, become 'impossible' when they do this.)
    Encourage the children to use their knowledge of bridging through 10 to bridge through 100:
8 + 7 = 8 + 2 + 5 = 10 + 5 = 15
so 80 + 70 = 80 + 20 + 50 = 100 + 50 = 150

DISCUSSION QUESTIONS
● *How do you add (for example) 50 and 20?*
● *How do you add (for example) 80 and 70?*

VARIATION
Begin with different combinations of numbers on the dice or spinners; for example, try with one marked 10, 30, 50, 70, 90, 100 and the other 0, 20, 40, 60, 80, 100.

EXTENSIONS
● The children can use the writing frame on photocopiable page 64 to reflect on their strategies.
● Use three dice, each marked 10, 20, 30, 40, 50, 60.
● Use three dice with a variety of multiples of ten up to 90. The number line should be extended to 300 for this.

CONSECUTIVE

†† *Whole class, then groups of 3*
⏲ *20–30 minutes for each investigation*

AIM
To investigate patterns in the addition of consecutive numbers.

WHAT TO DO
Start with a general examination of a number line, noting pairs of **consecutive** numbers such as 7 and 8 or 23 and 24. Ask the children what they notice about any pair. Useful facts to draw out are that one number is one more or one less than the other and that one number is **odd** and the other **even.**
    Let the children, working in groups of three, try one or more of these investigations:
● `Add any two consecutive numbers. What do you notice about the answer?'
● 'Find the two consecutive numbers that total 11, 21, 31... 81, 91. What do you notice?'
● 'Add two consecutive numbers. Then add the next two (eg 7 and 8, then 9 and 10). What is the difference between the two pairs? Does this always happen? Why?'
● 'Add any three consecutive numbers. Can you predict whether the answer will be odd or even?'
● 'Add pairs of consecutive odd numbers (eg 5 and 7). What do you notice? Look at the number in between your two numbers – how is that connected to your answer? Does this always happen for pairs of consecutive odd numbers? What about pairs of consecutive even numbers?'

DISCUSSION QUESTIONS
● *How did you add them? How did you check?*
● *Can you explain any patterns in your answers?*

STEPPING STONES

†† *Pairs* ⏱ *20–30 minutes*

AIM
To practise addition and subtraction using bridging and partitioning strategies.

YOU WILL NEED
For each pair: a long strip of paper marked '0' at one end and '50' at the other; a set of 1–50 number cards.

WHAT TO DO
This activity is described using numbers up to 50 but younger or less able children could begin with numbers up to 30 and older or more able children could work with numbers up to 100. The first time the children play this game, you should work through an example with the whole class.

The cards are shuffled and five are drawn at random. These should then be placed in order between the 0 and 50 on the paper strip. The number cards represent 'stepping stones' across an imaginary stream. One child should now calculate the steps from 0 to 50, the other from 50 to 0. For example, if the cards drawn are 6, 11, 23, 39, 41, the stepping stones can be ordered and the steps worked out as shown in Figure 4.

Figure 4

1st child's answers:
6, 5, 12, 16, 2, 9.

2nd child's answers:
9, 2, 16, 12, 5, 6.

The pair should then agree on the answers for the different steps, before shuffling the cards and repeating as before (with their roles reversed).

DISCUSSION QUESTIONS
● *Which steps were easy to work out? Why?*
● *Which steps were more difficult to work out? Why?*
● *Do you prefer starting at 0 or starting at 50? Does it matter?*
● *How can you check your steps? (They should add up to 50.)*

VARIATIONS
● Select more cards – this will produce a greater number of smaller jumps.
● Select fewer cards – this will produce a smaller number of bigger jumps.

TENS OR UNITS

†† *Pairs* ⏱ *15 minutes per round, 2 or 3 rounds*

AIM
To practise adding and subtracting tens and units.

YOU WILL NEED
For each pair: two dice – one marked 1, 1, 2, 2, 3, 3, the other marked T, T, T, U, U, U ('T' represents 'tens' and 'U' represents 'units'). Each player also needs a set of arrow cards (photocopiable page 62). Photocopiable page 64 could also be used.

WHAT TO DO
Each player starts at 99, using arrow cards to record her/his position. The aim is to finish as close to 55 as possible after ten throws of the dice. Players take it in turns to throw the dice. They can choose to take away or add the number of tens or units that comes up. For example, if '2' and 'tens' were thrown on the first throw, the player can swap the 'ninety' arrow card for the 'seventy'. Later, if a player has 32 and throws a '3' and a 'unit', he/she can swap the 'two' arrow card for the 'five'. It is important that the arrow cards are used to keep track of running totals; if children are unsure how to do this, play a demonstration game with them first. After ten throws, each player finds the difference between her/his number and 55. The player who was closest wins.

The children can use the writing frame on photocopiable page 64 to reflect on the activity prior to a group discussion.

DISCUSSION QUESTIONS

After several rounds of the game, have a session where you ask questions such as:
● *You have 23 and you add 3 tens. What number do you have now?*
● *You have 74 and you take away 2 tens. What number do you have now?*

VARIATION

The children could also use base blocks or a spike abacus to keep track of their current total.

EXTENSION

Extend the game to include hundreds. The second dice should now be labelled H, H, T, T, U, U. Players should start at 999 and aim at the target number 555.

TARGET 21

†† *Pairs* ⏱ *20 minutes*

AIM

To practise addition by regrouping numbers.

YOU WILL NEED

For each pair: two dice; a supply of blank cards; counters; marker pens.

WHAT TO DO

The children take it in turns to throw the two dice and add the numbers, recording the sum on a blank card. Each child keeps her/his own cards and must add together the numbers on some of these to make exactly 21. Players may use any combination of their own cards, but not all the

cards have to be used. For example, a player who throws the sums 5, 9, 6, 8 and then 6 can now make 21 using 9, 6 and 6.

The first person to make the target number receives a counter. The cards are then discarded and a new round starts. The loser in the previous round gets to throw first in the next one. The first child to collect five counters wins the game.

DISCUSSION QUESTIONS

● *What number do you need to throw to reach 21?*
● *What would be the quickest possible way for you to get 21?*

VARIATIONS

● The first player to reach 21 can set a new target number (40 would be a sensible maximum).
● Players can use numbers from each other's cards as well as their own.

EXTENSIONS

● The children can use the writing frame on photocopiable page 64 to reflect on their strategies.
● Allow subtraction, so that a player with 8, 7, 3 and 9 could make 21 as 8 + 7 + 9 – 3.
● Use three dice and have larger target numbers (up to 100).

BEAT THE CALCULATOR

†† *Groups of 3* ⏱ *20–30 minutes*

AIM

To practise selecting appropriate addition and subtraction strategies.

YOU WILL NEED

Several prepared sets of 10 questions – addition, subtraction or both. Write each question on a separate card. Each set of 10 should have a similar range of questions, from the clearly easy to the more challenging. Figure 5 shows a suitable range of questions for Year 3/Primary 4 and Year 4/Primary 5. Each group will also need a calculator, pencils and paper.

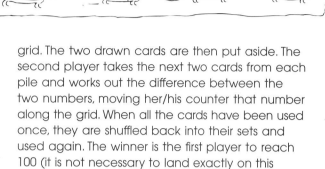

WHAT TO DO

In each group of three, one child reads the questions, one child calculates the answers mentally and one child works the answers out on a calculator. After each answer has been agreed, a tally should be made to record who answered first. After all the questions have been answered, the children should change roles, shuffle the cards and then repeat as before. After three rounds, they should stop and sort the questions into those that were quicker to do mentally and those that were more quickly done on the calculator. They should then focus on this second group, devising strategies to 'beat the calculator' for these questions. Then give them another set of questions to try out.

DISCUSSION QUESTIONS

● *Which questions are easier to do without a calculator? Why?*
● *What would be a good way to do that without a calculator?*

Figure 5

EXTENSIONS

● The children could use the writing frame on photocopiable page 64 to reflect on their strategies.
● Include simple addition triples such as 6 + 4 + 7.
● Include more complicated bridging questions such as 28 + 16 (see page 21).

For Y3/P4	For Y4/P5
5 + 3	4 + 5
9 – 2	9 – 7
7 + 4	8 + 7
13 – 6	17 – 8
15 + 5	18 + 12
24 – 10	17 + 16
18 + 4	23 – 8
21 + 20	24 – 17
26 – 9	32 – 18
16 + 17	16 + 37

THE DIFFERENCE RACE

†† *Pairs* ⏱ *20 minutes*

AIM

To practise subtraction using known number facts and complementary addition.

YOU WILL NEED

For each pair: one copy of the race grid (photocopiable page 60); two counters or markers; two sets of ten cards – one set numbered 1–10, the other set numbered 11–20 in a different colour.

WHAT TO DO

Shuffle the two sets of cards separately and put the two piles face down in front of the players. The first player turns over the top card from each set and works out the difference between the two numbers, moving her/his counter that number along the grid. The two drawn cards are then put aside. The second player takes the next two cards from each pile and works out the difference between the two numbers, moving her/his counter that number along the grid. When all the cards have been used once, they are shuffled back into their sets and used again. The winner is the first player to reach 100 (it is not necessary to land exactly on this number). The loser can begin the next game.

DISCUSSION QUESTIONS

● *Which are the best combinations of numbers to get? Which are not so good? Why?*
● *Which are easy subtractions to do? Which are trickier?*
● *How do you work out where to move your counter to?*

VARIATIONS

● Other pairs of sets of cards which could be tried are: 6–10 and 11–15; 6–10 and 16–20; 11–20 and 21–30.
● The players start at 100 and move backwards – the first player to get back to 1 wins.
● Play the same game on a 0–100 number line.

EXTENSIONS

● Combine both sets of cards, shuffle the pack and deal it into two equal face-down piles. Each player takes two cards as before, subtracting the first number from the second. Players will thus have a mixture of positive and negative numbers, leading to forward and backward moves on the board. They could start at 50 and aim to be the furthest from 50 (in either direction) after ten turns.
● Play the game with a variety of sets of cards, and investigate which sets are more likely to produce quicker wins.
● Ask each pair to choose ten numbers at random between 20 and 50, and work together to create a 'Snakes and ladders' game using these. The numbers represent the differences between the top and bottom of the ladder or the mouth and tail of the snake. The children have to determine corresponding 'start' and 'finish' numbers that give rise to these differences in order to place five snakes and five ladders on their boards. Let the pairs swap boards to play each other's games. What makes for a good 'Snakes and ladders' game?

STRATEGIES

CHILDREN SHOULD BE WORKING WITH NUMBERS OF THE ORDER:

YEAR 3/PRIMARY 4

● use knowledge of halving numbers to find quarters of familiar numbers;
● know and use knowledge of multiplication and division facts in the 2, 5 and 10 times table and other facts to 5 × 5;
● multiply familiar numbers by multiples of 10 (eg 3 × 20 = 60);
● understand and use the concept of remainders.

YEAR 4/PRIMARY 5

● express remainders as fractions if appropriate;
● extend knowledge of multiplication facts by powers of 10, (eg 3 × 6 = 18 so 3 × 60 = 180, 30 × 6 = 180 and 30 × 60 = 1800);
● calculate fractional amounts of familiar quantities, using fractions (halves, quarters, fifths and tenths) that correspond to familiar times tables.

AS A MINIMUM, BY THE END OF YEAR 4/PRIMARY 5, MOST CHILDREN SHOULD:

● know and use the doubles of all numbers to 20, and then 50, and the halves of these numbers, as well as the halves of all the even numbers to 100;
● know and use the multiplication and division facts in the 2, 3, 4, 5 and 10 times tables.

At this stage, it is vital to build up strong visual images that correspond to the structures of multiplication and division (the various grouping and sharing activities that children have undertaken in the early years). The images of these operations are not as obvious as those of addition and subtraction, and time needs to be spent consolidating them. Secondly, we need to create an expectation that certain multiplication and division facts (the 'times tables') will be memorised, and that these facts will also be used as building blocks for more complicated and sophisticated calculations.

Language: As children work in a variety of multiplication and division situations, we need to help them to make links between the language used and the underlying mathematical structures.

Important vocabulary: times, product, of, double, halve, share, group, left over, remainder.

STRATEGIES FOR MULTIPLICATION

Learning 'times tables' can be approached positively through emphasising patterns and relationships, and can be extended into tests for divisibility. The following general rules can be used to predict divisibility:

2 × table: all products are even;
4 × table: all products are even and are double those in the 2 × table;
8 × table: products are double those in the 4 × table;
3 × table: products are alternately even and odd (3, 6, 9, 12 ...);
6 × table: products are double those in the 3 × table;
9 × table: the ten and unit digit always total 9;
5 × table: products end alternately in 5 and 0;
10 × table: the unit digit is always 0, products in the 10 × table are double those in the 5 × table.

Using doubles:

calculating 3 × 6 from knowing that
2 × 6 = 12 and adding on another 6 or doubling
3 × 7 to find 6 × 7

Using repeated doubling:

solving 13 × 4 by doubling 13 (= 26) and
doubling again (= 52)

Using the effect of multiplying numbers by 10:

calculating 20 × 7 as 2 × 7 × 10

Partitioning two-digit numbers to multiply a
two-digit number by a single-digit number:

calculating 26 × 3 as (20 × 3) + (6 × 3)

Children need to be aware of the distributive
law which is being applied when numbers
are partitioned in this way: multiplication is
'distributed out' over addition.

STRATEGIES FOR DIVISION

Using known facts:

finding half of 46 is 23, since half of 40 is 20
and half of 6 is 3

Using repeated halving:

solving 100 ÷ 4 by halving 100 (= 50) and
halving again (= 25)

Using known multiplication facts:

28 ÷ 7 = 4, since 4 × 7 = 28
180 ÷ 3 = 60, since 18 ÷ 3 = 6

Partitioning larger numbers:

solving 116 ÷ 4 as (100 ÷ 4) + (16 ÷ 4) = 25 + 4
= 29

As above, children need to be aware of the
distributive law which is being applied here.

MULTIPLICATION AND DIVISION

SHAPING UP

†† *Whole class*
🕐 *15 minutes, several times over a half-term*

AIMS
To build up mental images for multiplication. To reinforce knowledge of the patterns in multiplication facts.

WHAT TO DO
Ask the children each to imagine a triangle and then discuss what their triangles look like: *'Is your triangle pointed? Is it tall? Is it wide? Is it right-angled? Is it coloured or transparent?'* Go on to ask the children what their triangles all have in common, three corners and three straight sides. Now ask the children to imagine a second triangle and to count the total number of sides (six), then a third and a fourth triangle and so on. Continue building up until the children have visualised up to 10 triangles, adding up the total number of sides as each triangle is imagined. If the children find this difficult, then draw the successive triangles.

In subsequent sessions, after the scene has been set by imagining one or two triangles and counting the sides, go on to imagining different **multiples** of three (thus rehearsing the three times table); or start with ten triangles and let the children remove them one by one.

Alternatively, use an image of a quadrilateral, pentagon, hexagon, heptagon, octagon or nonagon in the same way. If children are unfamiliar with these, or unsure which shape is which, then spend some time examining, drawing and naming them in a prior session.

DISCUSSION QUESTIONS
● *How many more sides will there be if you add another triangle? How do you know?*
● *Imagine seven triangles. What is a quick way to count the number of sides?*
● *I've got five identical shapes with 20 sides altogether. What shape am I thinking of?*

EXTENSIONS
● Mix up questions involving different shapes – for example: *'I'm imagining six hexagons, how many sides? I'm imagining four quadrilaterals, how many sides?...'*
● Explore the relationships between the numbers of sides in different shapes.

JUMPING UP THE LINE

†† *Whole class*
🕐 *15 minutes, several times over a half-term*

AIMS
To build up mental images for multiplication. To reinforce knowledge of the patterns in multiplication facts.

WHAT TO DO
The investigation 'Counters on a line' (page 46) should be undertaken in conjunction with this activity.

Ask the children to imagine a giant number line, across the playground or hall, going from 0 to 50. Now ask the children to imagine they are at zero and are going to jump in 3s or 4s along the line. What numbers will they be stopping at? Explain that these are called **multiples** of whatever number they were jumping in. When the children are confidently reciting the multiples, ask them to check which is the tenth multiple (30 or 40); then get them to jump back by the same multiples to 0.

Now ask them to jump to different multiples of 3 or 4, in a random order, thus rehearsing a variety of multiplication facts.

This image can be used to explore multiples of other numbers. For 6 and above, the number line will have to be extended for more than eight jumps; but let the children discover this for themselves (and, indeed, make the fact a point for subsequent discussion).

DISCUSSION QUESTION
Are there quick ways to find where a particular number of jumps will take you? (For example, 6 jumps of 3 – if you know that 5 jumps gets you to 15, then the answer will be 15 + 3 (or 18).

EXTENSIONS
● Try having half the class jumping in 2s and the other half in 4s. If they all make the same number of jumps, what do they notice about where they are on the number line? (Any given multiple of 4 is double the corresponding multiple of 2.)
● Try as above with the class divided into 3s and 6s, 5s and 10s or 4s and 8s.

VARIATION
Start the activity with a division fact, such as 30 ÷ 6 = 5.

EXTENSION
Tell the children about the imaginary numbers blab, blug and blunder. If blab multiplied by blug equals blunder, what else can they say about the three numbers?

WHAT ELSE DO YOU KNOW?

†† *Whole class*
🕐 *15 minutes; repeated several times over a half-term*

AIM
To link multiplication and division as inverses.

YOU WILL NEED
A board (or overhead projector).

WHAT TO DO
Write three numbers on the board, creating a number sentence to express a familiar multiplication fact such as 3 × 5 = 15. Ask the children to suggest other ways of combining these numbers using the question: 'What else do you know?'

Prompt if necessary: what if the 15 was divided? What if you swapped the 3 and the 5 around? Aim to draw out the following number facts, all related to the original fact:

5 × 3 = 15	15 ÷ 5 = 3	15 ÷ 3 = 5

Repeat for one or two other combinations, such as 4, 6 and 24 or 2, 8 and 16. Then ask the children to suggest another multiplication fact to explore in the same way.

DISCUSSION QUESTIONS
● *How else can you rewrite the numbers?*
● *Are you sure you've found all the ways?*

TENS ARE EASY

†† *Whole class*   🕐 *15 minutes, several times*

AIM
To practise multiplying by tens.

YOU WILL NEED
A board (or overhead projector).

WHAT TO DO
Warm the class up by counting around the room in tens, up to 200 and back.

Consider the questions 3 × 10 and 8 × 10, then 13 × 10 and 24 × 10. Write the answers as a list:

3   → 30
8   → 80
13 → 130
24 → 240

Visually, it is clear why multiplying whole numbers by 10 is so easy: 'You add a nought.' However, children need to rehearse giving explanations in terms of place value, since 'adding a nought' breaks down when decimals are involved. To do this, it is best to focus initially on a two-digit number such as 24. What has happened to the 20? It's now 200. What has happened to the 4? It's now 40. Thus the nought acts as a place holder. This can be made clearer by using 'HTU' headings or by modelling with base 10 blocks: 2 tens become 2 hundreds and 4 units become 4 tens.

In subsequent sessions, recap this 'place value' explanation before looking at the effect of multiplying other numbers, up to hundreds, by 10.

MULTIPLICATION AND DIVISION

DISCUSSION QUESTIONS
● *Who can explain how to multiply by 10?*
● *What happens to the digits?*
● *If 23 is multiplied by 10, what happens to the 2? What happens to the 3?*
Look for answers in terms of units, tens and hundreds.

EXTENSIONS
● Lead a session of multiplying three-digit numbers by 10.
● Lead a session of multiplying by 20 as multiplying by 10 and then doubling (or vice versa).

$$20 \times 13 = 2 \times 10 \times 13 = 2 \times 130 = 260$$
$$\text{or } 26 \times 10 = 260$$

● Lead a session of multiplying by 5 as multiplying by 10 and halving.

$$5 \times 13 = \text{half of } 10 \times 13 = 130 \div 2 = 65$$

AMONG THE TWELVES

†† *Whole class*
⊕ *15 minutes, several times over a half-term*

AIM
To develop strategies for multiplying a two-digit number by a single digit.

YOU WILL NEED
A board (or overhead projector).

WHAT TO DO
Tell the children about the days when people really needed to learn the 12 times table, because twelves were used in money (shillings and pence) and in length (feet and inches). Explain that you are going to show them a way to work out the twelve times table so that they never have to learn it by heart.

Write the number 12 on the board and ask questions about the 1 digit. When it is clearly agreed that this digit stands for 10, rewrite the 12 as 10 + 2. Tell the children that as they know the 10 and the 2 times tables, working out twelves will be easy. Now write up 12 × 4. Ask what 10 × 4 is, then 2 × 4, and finally what 40 + 8 is. Work through this strategy for other multiplications of 12, in a random order. In each case, ask the children to state what the two separate parts are that are added together.

The value of this method (which might seem tedious to those of us who learned the 12 times table by rote) is that the same principle can be

applied to any two-digit number; and that by selecting appropriate questions, you can examine this method with the children before they have fluency in the 6 to 9 times tables. Sessions could focus on multiplying 13, 14 or 15 in the same way, for example:

$$13 \times 3 = (10 \times 3) + (3 \times 3) = 30 + 9 = 39$$
$$14 \times 5 = (10 \times 5) + (4 \times 5) = 50 + 20 = 70$$

DISCUSSION QUESTIONS
● *Why is the ten times table easy?*
● *What other times tables do you know?*

EXTENSION
Multiply larger two-digit numbers using the same principle of multiplying the tens first, for example:
$$32 \times 6 = (30 \times 6) + (2 \times 6) = 180 + 12 = 192.$$

GET IN GROUPS

†† *Whole class*
⊕ *20–25 minutes initial activity, several 20-minute follow-up sessions*

AIM
To build up a conceptual model of division with remainders.

YOU WILL NEED
Several PE mats; the school hall or other large space appropriate for PE work.

WHAT TO DO
The investigation 'The big share-out' (page 47) should be undertaken in conjunction with this activity.

Part 1
Lay out a number of mats around the hall. Choose the initial number of mats such that the children will be able to divide equally between them – if

necessary, join in as a participant to make this possible. Ask the children to move on to the mats so that the same number of children are on each one. Allow time for the children to negotiate this; check by nominating a captain on each mat to do a final count. If the numbers on the mats are not equal, ask how many need to move. Now model what has happened using the language of division – for example, twenty-seven children divided between three mats or 27 ÷ 3 = 9.

Ask the children to predict what would happen if you had one more or one less mat, then try this out practically. Introduce the term **remainder** for any children left out when there is the same number on each mat. Let these children be the 'mat captains' in the next round. Add or remove mats so that by the end of the activity the class have divided themselves by all the numbers from 2 up to 8 or 9. Encourage predictions before each round.

To stimulate further discussion, ask what would have happened if one or two children had been away, or if any actual absentees had been present.

Part 2

In subsequent classroom sessions, draw on the above activity to ask division questions, beginning with straightforward ones and progressing to ones that are more open-ended. (See 'Discussion questions' below.)

DISCUSSION QUESTIONS

● 21 children divided between 3 mats – how many on each? Any remainder?
● 26 children divided between 5 mats – how many on each? Any remainder?
● How many mats could we have for 24 children such that there is no remainder? Is any number of mats possible?
● If there are four mats, what number of children would give no remainder?

EXTENSION

Ask the children to find out, for a given number of mats (for example four, five or six), which numbers of children give particular remainders (for example 1, 2 or 3). They could draw diagrams of the mats to show possible solutions.

EVEN UP THE ODDS

†† *Whole class*
⏱ *15 minutes, several times over a half-term*

AIM
To explore pattern in multiplication facts.

YOU WILL NEED
A board (or overhead projector).

WHAT TO DO
Ask the children to say the **even** numbers up to 10. Write these up on the board. Ask the children whether they think the **product** of any two of these numbers will be even or odd. Pick any pair of the numbers and ask for the product. Write up the answer and repeat this several times. The children should examine the answers and comment.

Next, ask the children what they think will happen with the **odd** numbers up to 10. Again, write up the numbers and proceed as before. Finally, ask the children what they think will happen if an even number is multiplied by an odd number. Again, try several examples.

DISCUSSION QUESTIONS
● *Does the same thing happen when you multiply larger numbers (using a calculator)?*
● *Can you explain all the rules for multiplying odd and even numbers? (Even × even = even; odd × odd = odd; even × odd = odd × even = even.)*
● *If the product of two numbers is odd, what can you tell about the numbers?*
● *If the product of two numbers is even, what can you tell about the numbers?*

EXTENSIONS
● Investigate the results of multiplying three numbers together – three odd, three even, two even with one odd, two odd with one even. (The results will always be odd, even, even and even respectively.)
● Imagine a game in which two dice are thrown. One player gets a point if the product is even; the other gets a point if the product is odd. Is this a fair game? Can you explain why not? (It is not a fair game since there is a greater likelihood of getting an even number: to get an odd number product, *both* of the numbers thrown have to be odd.)

ASK ME A QUESTION

†† *Pairs* ⏱ *30 minutes*

AIM

To recognise and develop contexts for multiplication problems.

WHAT TO DO

Give the children some examples of word problems that require a multiplication calculation to find the answer, such as:

> 'If there are six eggs in a box and I buy three boxes, how many eggs do I have?'
> 'How much will I pay for four chews if each costs four pence?'
> 'My car is three metres long; if twenty similar cars were in a line, how far would that stretch?'

Now give the children some multiplication problems in pure numerical form, such as 5 × 9 or 23 × 6. These should reflect the times tables that currently concern you, or other multiplication strategies you wish to promote (see page 36). Give three or four different calculations to each pair, asking them to write some word problems for each calculation. They should be encouraged to draft and redraft these as they would any other piece of writing.

The children should swap their final versions with other pairs and solve each other's questions. The written problems can be collected together for a class book or display.

DISCUSSION QUESTIONS

● *How did you solve the problem? How can you check your answer?*
● *Read your question again. Are you sure it makes sense?*

EXTENSION

Repeat the above activity with division word problems, for example:

> 'If four pencils cost 32p, how much would each one cost?'
> 'There are thirty children in the class. How many teams of five can they make?'

YOU AND A FRIEND

†† *Whole class*
⏱ *20 minutes, several times over a week*

AIM

To develop strategies for doubling.

YOU WILL NEED

Several items with price labels: a pen, a pencil, scissors, small toys, small grocery items and so on. Each item should be marked up with a cost less than 50p.

WHAT TO DO

Ask a child to choose one of the items. Read out the cost, then ask how much it would cost her to buy one for herself and one for her friend. Ask whether everyone agrees, and ask individual children to explain how they worked it out – different children will have different methods, and different amounts call for different strategies.

Where children have difficulty articulating their methods, model a few examples (using different strategies) for them. For instance:

> Two items at 24p each – 2 times 20 equals 40, 2 times 4 equals 8, so total cost is 48p.
> Two items at 35p each – 5 and 5 make 10, plus 30 is 40 and another 30 makes 70p.
> Two items at 28p each – 28 plus 20 makes 48, add 2 add 6 makes 56p.

DISCUSSION QUESTIONS

● *How do you double 10p, 20p, 30p or 40p?*
● *Which other amounts are easy to double? Which are more difficult?*

EXTENSIONS

● Include items costing more than 50p.
● After the cost for two people has been agreed, ask how much it would cost to buy one of the item for another pair of people (four people in all), thus rehearsing successive doubling as a strategy for multiplying by four.

HALF PRICE SALE

†† *Whole class*
🕑 *20 minutes, several times over a week*

AIM

To develop strategies for halving.

YOU WILL NEED

As in 'You and a friend' (page 42), prepare price labels for several items: a pen, a pencil, scissors, small toys, small grocery items and so on. To begin with, the items should be marked in ten pence units, ie 10p, 20p, 30p, up to 90p.

WHAT TO DO

Tell the children that everything in the shop is now on sale at half price. Ask a child to choose one of the items. Read out the cost, then ask how much it will cost in the sale. The children should be encouraged, through questioning, to see that the new cost is either a multiple of 10p or 'something 5'. A table of 'halving' can be drawn up to make this clear (see Figure 1). This is worth emphasising over a couple of sessions, since the strategy suggested for halving other amounts will build on this knowledge.

Figure 1

Original price	10p	20p	30p	40p	50p	60p	70p	80p	90p
Half price	5p	10p	15p	20p	25p	30p	35p	40p	45p

When the children are confident about halving whole tens, introduce other amounts (keeping the initial costs of the items to even numbers of pence. Repeat as before by asking a child to choose one of the items, reading out the cost and then asking how much it will cost in the half price sale. Ask children to explain how they calculated the new sale price. Where children have difficulty articulating their methods, you should model the following method which builds on the facts in Figure 1. (This method uses the partition strategy described on page 37, which assumes that multiplication can be distributed across the addition complements of a number.)

● Original cost 24p. Half of 20p is 10p, half of 4p is 2p, so half of 24p is 10p + 2p = 12p.
● Original cost 36p. Half of 30p is 15p, half of 6p is 3p, so half of 36p is 15p + 3p = 18p.
● Original cost 78p. Half of 70p is 35p, half of 8p is 4p, so half of 78p is 35p + 4p = 39p.

DISCUSSION QUESTIONS

● *How do you find half of 10p, 20p, 30p?*
● *What patterns can you see by comparing the half price costs to the full prices?*
● *Which numbers are easy to halve? Which are more complicated?*

EXTENSIONS

● Include items with odd-numbered costs (as we no longer use the $\frac{1}{2}$p coin, it seems sensible to suggest that halves are rounded up to the next penny).
● Include items costing more than £1.

RECTANGLE AREAS

†† *Whole class*
🕑 *20 minutes, several sessions over a week*

AIM

To use rectangular arrays to explore the relationship between multiplication and division.

YOU WILL NEED

A board (or overhead projector).

WHAT TO DO

Draw up some rectangles on the board, clearly showing their constituent squares (see left). In the initial stages it is not necessary to use standard units (cm), but the distinction between horizontal **rows** and vertical **columns** should be explained.

Ask the children to count the squares in each rectangle. Then ask whether there is a quicker way to do this than just counting, drawing out the fact that, for any rectangle, multiplying the number of columns by the number of

MULTIPLICATION AND DIVISION

rows gives the total number of squares. Then use the rectangle model to rehearse multiplication facts, for example:

> If a rectangle has 4 rows of squares and 3 columns, how many squares are there altogether?
> If a rectangle has 3 rows of squares and 6 columns, how many squares are there altogether?

When the children can answer these confidently, go on to division questions such as:

> Imagine a rectangle with 10 squares in 2 columns. How many rows are there?
> Imagine a rectangle with 20 squares in 5 rows. How many columns are there?

If children are unsure of how to answer any question, draw up the appropriate rectangle to work through the problem.

In later sessions, mix up the multiplication and division questions and make the explicit connections between multiplication and division facts, eg if $4 \times 5 = 20$ then $20 \div 4 = 5$. (Also see 'What else do you know?' on page 39).

DISCUSSION QUESTION

Compare the number of squares in a 4 by 5 rectangle and a 5 by 4 rectangle. Does this happen for any pair of numbers?

VARIATION

The children *could* start by individually drawing rectangles on squared paper – but this should then be followed up by a session spent visualising and calculating mentally, in order to emphasise that the rectangles are a model for multiplication.

EXTENSIONS (FOR YEAR 4/PRIMARY 5)

● Introduce units – cm, cm², m, m² – and use length and width rather than numbers of columns and rows. Pose multiplication and division problems in measurement contexts, for example:

> A playing card is 6cm long and 3cm wide. What is its area?
> A rectangular room has a floor area of 20m². If the length is 4m, what is the width?

● Introduce larger numbers: 14 by 4 or 23 by 3. (See page 37 for strategies for this type of question).

WHAT'S IN THE CUBOID?

✝✝ *Groups*
🕐 *Duration 30–40 minutes (over 2 or 3 sessions)*

AIM

To use and extend strategies for multiplying and dividing using cuboids.

YOU WILL NEED

For each group: one $2 \times 3 \times 4$ cuboid (made from 24 Multilink cubes); a further supply of Multilink cubes.

WHAT TO DO

Distribute the cuboids between the groups. Ask each group to see if they can agree on how many Multilink cubes are in the cuboid. (They are not allowed to take it apart.) Ask for explanations – did they have to count them all? Are there quicker ways of working it out?

Now give the groups a bigger supply of Multilink cubes and ask them to construct a cuboid with 36 cubes. They should try to predict what the dimensions will be before they make it. At this stage, it is not necessary to use standard units of measurement; but the words *length*, *width* and *height* should be used.

Groups should compare their cuboids: do they all have the same dimensions? (Some might be the same but in different orientations.) How many different cuboids can be made with 36 cubes? The children should look at **length**, **width** and **height** and express these dimensions as, for example, '*2 by 3 by 6*', linking the word '*by*' to multiplication. Don't forget that one of the dimensions might be 1, so possible answers include $1 \times 4 \times 9$ and even $1 \times 1 \times 36$.

Different groups could follow this up for different numbers of cubes – try 20, 27, 40 or 48.

Ask them to explain how they worked this out. They should also note any that are impossible to make, for example a 30-cube model with equal numbers of four colours or a 20-cube model with equal numbers of three colours; they should be encouraged to explain these findings.

In a later session, use the cuboid model to ask questions about fractional amounts (see 'Discussion questions'). The children could pose similar questions about their own models.

DISCUSSION QUESTIONS
● *Imagine a cuboid made from 24 Multilink cubes. One third are yellow; how many cubes is that?*
● *A cuboid has five green cubes, which is one quarter of the total; how many cubes does it have altogether?*

VARIATION
Make other models using Multilink – a robot, a dog or a tower – such that the model is half, a third or a quarter in any particular colour.

EXTENSION (YEAR 4/PRIMARY 5)
Ask the children to use only two colours for thirds and quarters, so that a cuboid could be (for example) one-third red and two-thirds green. Later, ask them to find two-thirds and three-quarters of various numbers mentally by visualising their Multilink models.

EXTENSIONS (YEAR 4/PRIMARY 5)
● Follow up this activity with a purely mental session asking questions such as: '*I want you to imagine a cuboid that is made of twenty small cubes; the width and the length are both two cubes long. What is the height?*'
● Introduce units – cm and cm^3 – and let the children measure small boxes and calculate their volume. Stock cube boxes and matchboxes are ideal for this.

MORE CUBOIDS

†† *Whole class, then groups*
⏰ *30–40 minutes (over 2 or 3 sessions)*

AIM
To develop strategies for finding halves, thirds and quarters using 3D models.

YOU WILL NEED
A 2 × 3 × 4 cuboid made from 24 Multilink cubes; a further supply of Multilink cubes.

WHAT TO DO
Show a 2 × 3 × 4 cuboid to the class. Set them the task of making a similar cuboid using only two, three or four colours of cubes and the same number of cubes of each colour. When they have done this, ask the children to talk about their cuboids using fractional language and link this to the numbers of cubes in the model. If necessary, model this: 'This cuboid is one half red, so one half of 24 is 12.'

Now ask groups to construct other cuboids (as in the previous activity), again using only two, three or four colours and equal numbers of each. They should discuss how many cubes of each colour will be needed before they make the cuboid.

MULTIPLICATION AND DIVISION

COUNTERS ON A LINE

†† *Pairs* 🕐 *20 minutes*

AIM
To explore pattern in the multiples of small numbers.

YOU WILL NEED
For each pair: a 0–100 number line (A3 copy of photocopiable page 63); some counters.

WHAT TO DO
The teacher-led activity 'Jumping up the line' (page 38) should be used before or in conjunction with this investigation. Ask the children to put a counter on 0, then another on every third, fourth or fifth number. They should make a note of which numbers the counters fall on and describe any patterns they notice. (With threes, the counters fall alternately on odd and even numbers. With fours, they always fall on even numbers. Fives give the alternate endings '5' and '0'.)

DISCUSSION QUESTIONS
● *How could you work out where to put the counters without counting on?*
● *Do you notice any patterns in the way the counters are placed?*

VARIATION
Try the same activity on a 100 square.

EXTENSIONS
● Look at multiples of 6, 7, 8 or 9 in the same way.
● Record multiples of two numbers, such as 3 and 4, in different colours on the same number line. This allows investigation of **common multiples**.

DICEY NUMBERS

†† *Pairs* 🕐 *20 minutes*

AIM
To explore multiplication facts.

YOU WILL NEED
For each pair: a 0–100 number line or 100 square; two ordinary dice.

WHAT TO DO
Working in pairs, the children should take turns to roll the two dice, calculate the **product** and mark that number off on the number line or square.

They should then investigate what numbers will be marked off if they continue throwing the dice and marking off the products – at first, they can do this by throwing the dice, but after a few minutes they should be challenged to come up with a strategy to find all the possible products. This could involve checking each number along the line or square; or working their way through all the dice combinations in a logical order. Each pair should then check their solution with another pair.

The possible products for two 1–6 dice are: 1, 2, 3, 4, 5, 6, 8, 9, 10, 12, 15, 16, 18, 20, 24, 25, 30, 36.

DISCUSSION QUESTIONS
● *What's the largest possible product? Why?*
● *Can you make 12, 19, 24, 26? Why/why not?*
● *How can you be sure that you've found all the possible products?*

VARIATION
Use different dice or pairs of spinners, such as two octahedron dice, two dice each marked 3–8 or two spinners marked 1–10.

EXTENSIONS
● Investigate which products have more than one possible solution – for example, 12 could be 4 × 3 or 6 × 2.
● Use three ordinary dice, multiplying the three numbers together to find the product. Does it matter in what order you multiply them together – for example, is 2 × 4 × 5 the same as 5 × 2 × 4?

RECTANGULAR NUMBERS

†† *Whole class and pairs* 🕐 *30 minutes*

AIM
To explore factors.

YOU WILL NEED
For each pair: a supply of counters or small cubes; some squared paper.

WHAT TO DO
Ask the children to count out 12 counters and arrange them to make a rectangle. Then ask whether there are other possible ways to make a rectangle with their 12 counters.

There will need to be some whole-class discussion to establish all the possible alternatives such as 1 × 12, 2 × 6 and 3 × 4. The children will need to understand that 3 rows of 4 counters are equivalent to 4 rows of 3 counters (recording on squared paper will help with this). Thus 1, 2, 3, 4, 6 and 12 are the **factors** of 12.

● *Challenge A* Now try with 9 counters. It will soon be established that one possible solution is 3 × 3, which is a **square**. Set the children the challenge of finding other **square numbers** using the counters.

● *Challenge B* Now try with 7 counters. It will soon be established that the only solution is 1 × 7, which is a single line or row of counters, since 7 has only two factors: 1 and itself. Set the children the challenge of finding other **prime numbers** using the counters – that is, the numbers of counters which can only be shown by a single line. They could work initially with numbers up to 50, then up to 100.

DISCUSSION QUESTIONS

Challenge A

● *Which numbers of counters can make squares? How can you check you have found all the possibilities up to 100? (Since 100 is 10 × 10, the children should check that they have included 9 × 9, 8 × 8, 7 × 7 and so on.)*

Challenge B

● *Do you notice anything about the different numbers of counters that can only be put into a single line? (All prime numbers above 2 are odd.)*

● *How did you check that there are no other solutions? (For example, dividing one of the factors by 2 or 3.)*

EXTENSIONS

● Starting with 4 (2 × 2), systematically build all the **square numbers** using the counters (or by drawing them on squared paper). What can be noticed about the way that each square number relates to the one before? (The difference between each pair goes up in successive odd numbers: 4 – 1 = 3, 9 – 4 = 5, 16 – 9 = 7 and so on.)

● Any number above 1 has at least two factors, itself and 1. Which numbers (up to 50 or 100) have the greatest number of factors? (48 has ten factors; 60, 72, 84, 90 and 96 each have twelve factors.)

● Do all numbers have an even number of factors? (Not square numbers.)

THE BIG SHARE-OUT

†† *Whole class, then pairs*   ⏱ *30 minutes*

AIM

To explore pattern in division.

YOU WILL NEED

For each pair: a supply of counters or small cubes; several sets of rings or carpet tiles (up to 9).

WHAT TO DO

This investigation complements the whole-class activity 'Get in groups' (page 40). It involves dividing a variable number of counters between a variable number of rings. To start with, the children should physically share out the counters and make a note of what happens. They should then be encouraged to predict what will happen as the number of rings and the number of counters is altered, then test their predictions.

Start with a whole-class example. Try 20 counters between two rings – the children should put 10 counters in each ring. Now try with three rings – six counters can go in each ring, with two left over. Use or introduce the term **remainder**. Now try with four rings or five rings. What about six or seven rings? Will the 20 counters share out equally, or will there be any left over?

Now give pairs of children different numbers of counters to investigate in the same way. They should always start with two rings and work systematically, adding one further ring at a time. For any number of counters, they should note which numbers of rings give no remainder (you could introduce the term **factor** here: the number of rings is a **factor** of the number of counters if all the counters can be share equally between the rings). Other patterns may be noticed – for example, dividing 20 by 3, 6 or 9 gives a remainder of 2 in each case.

DISCUSSION QUESTIONS

● *Do you think that you can divide that number between that number of rings? Why/why not?*

● *Are there other numbers that can be divided between 3/4/5 rings without any being left over?*

EXTENSIONS

● The children could use the writing frame on photocopiable page 64 to reflect on this activity.

● Find which numbers of counters cannot be shared between any number of rings other than the number itself – ie the **prime** numbers: 2, 3, 5, 7, 11, 13, 17, 19, 23, 29 and so on.

● Investigate which combinations of counters and rings will give a remainder of 1, then 2, 3 or 4.

DEVELOPING MENTAL MATHS

MULTIPLICATION AND DIVISION

MULTIPLICATION AND DIVISION

STAKE A CLAIM

†† Pairs ⏲ 15–20 minutes

AIM

To reinforce knowledge of multiplication bonds.

YOU WILL NEED

For each pair: a copy of the 5 × 5 grid shown in Figure 2; two sets of 1–5 digit cards; pens in two different colours.

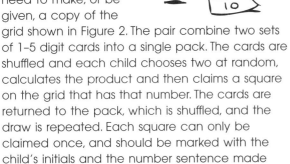

WHAT TO DO

Each pair of children need to make, or be given, a copy of the grid shown in Figure 2. The pair combine two sets of 1–5 digit cards into a single pack. The cards are shuffled and each child chooses two at random, calculates the product and then claims a square on the grid that has that number. The cards are returned to the pack, which is shuffled, and the draw is repeated. Each square can only be claimed once, and should be marked with the child's initials and the number sentence made (eg 3 × 4 = 12).

Play continues either for a fixed number of rounds or until all of the squares have been claimed. The claims should be checked; if any mistakes are made, the claim is discounted. The winner is the player with her/his initials in the most squares.

Figure 2

1	2	3	4	5
2	4	6	8	10
3	6	9	12	15
4	8	12	16	20
5	10	15	20	25

DISCUSSION QUESTION

Are you sure your initials should go there? Can you check that calculation?

Figure 3

1	2	3	4	5
2	4	6	8	10
3	6	9	12	15
4	8	12	16	20
5	10	15	20	25
6	12	18	24	30
7	14	21	28	35
8	16	24	32	40
9	18	27	36	45
10	20	30	40	50

EXTENSIONS

● The children could play on a 5 × 10 grid, as shown in Figure 3. They will need two separate sets of cards: a 1–5 set and a 1–10 set. In turn, one card should be drawn from each pile.

● The children could play on a 5 × 5 grid with the numbers arranged randomly rather than in a 'times table' format. This will prevent them from locating the answer by 'reading' the table.

BIG DICE, LITTLE DICE

†† Pairs ⏲ 15–20 minutes

AIM

To develop strategies for multiplying single-digit numbers by multiples of 10.

YOU WILL NEED

For each pair: an ordinary small dice and a larger dice marked 10, 20, 30, 40, 50 and 60; a copy of the number grid shown in Figure 4.

WHAT TO DO

Each pair of children need to make or be given a copy of the grid shown in Figure 4. The grid should be cut in half, either horizontally or vertically, and each player takes half of the grid.

Figure 4

10	20	30	40	50	60
20	40	60	80	100	120
30	60	90	120	150	180
40	80	120	160	200	240
50	100	150	200	250	300
60	120	180	240	300	360

The players take turns to throw both dice (simultaneously) and multiply the two numbers to find a target number. If either player has that target number, he/she can mark it off on his/her grid. Each player can only mark off **one** target number for each throw, and each square can only be marked off **once**. They should write the two dice numbers in the square, so that their calculations can later be checked.

Play continues for a fixed number of throws of the dice (such as 20). The player with more squares marked off is the winner.

DISCUSSION QUESTIONS

● *How do you multiply the two numbers? Is there another way of doing it that you could use to check your answer?*
● *What two dice numbers will multiply to give you (for example) 120? Are there other ways to make that answer using these dice?*

EXTENSIONS

● The children could use the writing frame on photocopiable page 64 to reflect on the strategies they have used.
● Challenge the children to recite the 20, 30, 40 or 50 times table (up to × 6). Then ask random questions based on these multiplication facts.

RACE TO 100

†† *Pairs* ⏱ *15–20 minutes*

AIM

To develop strategies for doubling and trebling.

YOU WILL NEED

For each pair: a 0–100 number line (photocopiable page 63, enlarged to A3); an ordinary 1–6 dice and a second dice marked 1, 1, 2, 2, 3, 3 (single, double and treble). For each player: a counter or other marker.

WHAT TO DO

Both players start at zero, taking it in turns to roll both the dice. The score is calculated by combining the two dice, eg 'double 3', 'treble 4', 'single 5'. With each turn, the player advances along the number line. The winner is the first to reach or pass 100.

DISCUSSION QUESTIONS

● *What is a good way to double/treble the numbers?*
● *Which dice is more important?*
● *How do you work out where to move your counter to? (The children should use addition rather than counting on – see the discussion of addition strategies on page 20.)*

VARIATION

Play the same game on the race grid (photocopiable page 60).

EXTENSIONS

● The children could use the writing frame on page 64 to reflect on their strategies.
● Start at 100 and work backwards to zero.
● Combine other dice or spinners with the 'single, double, treble' dice, such as a 3–8 dice or a 0, 2, 4, 6, 8, 10 spinner.

HIGH AND LOW

†† *Pairs or threes* ⏱ *20 minutes*

AIM

To develop strategies for, and visual/verbal fluency in, doubling and halving.

YOU WILL NEED

For each pair: a copy of the race grid (photocopiable page 60); two dice – one marked 2, 4, 6, 8, 10, 12 and the other marked × 2, double, twice, $\frac{1}{2}$, half, ÷ 2. (Mark up blank dice or use small labels; alternatively, make up spinners with these numbers and instructions). For each player: a counter or marker.

WHAT TO DO

The players take turns to throw both dice, determining their score by combining the number on the first dice with the operation on the second. They make their way around the race track, with the winner being the first to reach or pass 100.

DISCUSSION QUESTIONS

● *What is the best/worst combination of dice you can get?*
● *How do you work out where to move your counter to?*
● *What happens if you double a number, then halve the answer? What if you halve a number, then double it?*

VARIATION

● Start at 100 and move backwards – the first player to get back to 1 wins.
● Play the same game on a 0–100 number line.

EXTENSION

Try this game with dice marked 4, 8, 12, 16, 20, 24 and $\frac{1}{2}$, $\frac{1}{2}$, $\frac{1}{2}$, $\frac{1}{4}$, $\frac{1}{4}$, $\frac{1}{4}$. How does finding a quarter of a number compare with finding half?

STRATEGIES

CHILDREN SHOULD BE WORKING WITH NUMBERS OF THE ORDER:

See page 10 for counting and ordering, page 20 for addition and subtraction and page 36 for multiplication and division.

AS A MINIMUM, BY THE END OF YEAR 4/PRIMARY 5, MOST CHILDREN SHOULD BE ABLE:

● to count forwards and backwards in integer (whole number) steps of any size, below 0 if necessary;
● to count fractional chains including tenths (relating these to decimals);
● to read and order numbers to at least 1000;
● to know the value of numerals in numbers to 100 000;
● to read and order negative numbers;
● to recognise equivalence between common fractions (eg $\frac{6}{12}=\frac{1}{2}$, $\frac{3}{9}=\frac{1}{3}$, $\frac{25}{100}=\frac{1}{4}$);

For addition and subtraction

● to know and use addition facts to 20;
● to know and use doubles and halves of all numbers to 20;
● to know and use simple fractions;
● to recognise equivalent values of coins;
● to use decimals in the context of money and measures where the decimals are all of the same order (one or two decimal places, but not a mixture);

For multiplication and division

● to know and use doubles of all numbers to 20, and multiples of 10;
● to know and use halves of all numbers to 20, and of even numbers between 20 and 100;
● to know and use the 2, 3, 4, 5 and 10 times tables for multiplication and division;
● to express remainders as fractions where appropriate;
● to calculate fractional amounts of familiar quantities – the fractions used (halves, quarters, fifths and tenths) corresponding to familiar multiplication facts.

Further detail is given on page 10 for counting and ordering, page 20 for addition and subtraction and page 36 for multiplication and division.

Developing mental mathematics requires children to adopt strategies which are flexible and adaptable; it also requires them to achieve a firm grasp of each of the four operations (addition, subtraction, multiplication and division) by building up strong concepts linked to a variety of different visual images. The activities in this chapter concern the relationships between the four operations, and involve children in considering the distinct effects of each.

Language related to each of the operations can be summarised in the form of a table (see Figure 1), which could be used to make up a classroom poster. These lists are not exhaustive, and children can add in vocabulary as it is encountered; it is important that they recognise which operation is linked to which vocabulary.

Figure 1

+ addition more than and add increase sum of total	− subtraction less than take away minus decrease difference subtract
× multiplication square product of times multiply	÷ division how many times into share group split divide

The order of the numbers matters in some operations, but not in others.
Addition and multiplication are commutative:

$4 + 8 = 8 + 4$ and $4 \times 8 = 8 \times 4$

Subtraction and division are not commutative:

$8 - 4 \neq 4 - 8$; $8 \div 4 \neq 4 \div 8$

Number sizes: With whole numbers, adding and multiplying will increase the number whereas subtracting and dividing will reduce it. With multiplication and division, the effect is greater than with addition and subtraction:

$20 + 4 = 24$ and $20 \times 4 = 80$;
$20 - 4 = 16$ and $20 \div 4 = 5$

Multistep problems: Where children are required to perform two (or more) operations in quick succession, they need to develop techniques for holding on to the interim number. Consider this example:

Start with 7, add 2, then multiply by 5.
$7 + 2 = 9$ and $9 \times 5 = 45$

Children can jot down the 9. If they then check the answer by retracing their steps, the 9 should reappear: $45 \div 5 = 9$ and $9 - 2 = 7$. This draws on their understanding of inverses.

STRATEGIES FOR MULTISTEP AND MIXED OPERATIONS PROBLEMS

The relationships between the four operations should be reinforced.
Addition and subtraction are inverse operations:

$9 + 3 = 12$ and $12 - 3 = 9$

Multiplication and division are inverse operations:

$9 \times 3 = 27$ and $27 \div 3 = 9$

Multiplication can be seen as repeated addition:

$4 \times 3 = 3 + 3 + 3 + 3 = 12$

Division can be seen as repeated subtraction:

$12 \div 3$ can be solved by working out $12 - 3 - 3 - 3 - 3 = 0$ so there are four 3s in 12, so $12 \div 3 = 4$.

These four relationships can be summarised in the form of a diagram:

$$
\begin{array}{ccc}
+ & \longleftrightarrow & - \\
\downarrow & & \downarrow \\
\times & \longleftrightarrow & \div
\end{array}
$$

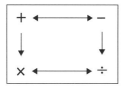

ALL THE THREES AND FOURS

†† *Whole class*

🕐 *20 minutes, several times over a fortnight*

AIM

To develop strategies for combining multiples.

WHAT TO DO

After a short warm-up involving a quick recall of the three and four times tables, ask questions which involve combinations of these multiplication facts:

● *'What are two 3s plus two 4s?'*
● *'What are three 4s plus one 3?'*
● *'What are two 4s plus three 3s?'*

(A useful strategy here is to ask the children to check each solution with a neighbour before putting up their hand to answer.)

When the children are answering confidently, ask similar questions in reverse: *'How can I make 14/16/17/18 with either just 3s or 4s or a combination of 3s and 4s?'*

DISCUSSION QUESTIONS

● *How did you add the numbers together?*
● *How did you find the right combination?*
● *Are there other ways to make that total?*

VARIATION

This activity can be linked to the investigation 'Make up the numbers' (page 56), which involves exploring combinations of Unifix lengths.

EXTENSIONS

● Try with other number combinations, such as 2s and 5s, 3s and 5s or 4s and 5s.
● Work though all the totals up to 30 for any pair of numbers.
● The children could use the writing frame on photocopiable page 64 to record their strategies.

A AND B

†† *Whole class* 🕐 *20 minutes*

AIMS

To develop strategies for finding unknowns. To develop strategies for checking solutions.

WHAT TO DO

Prepare two A4 cards clearly marked 'A' and 'B'. Without letting the children see, write the numbers 2 and 3 on small pieces of paper and attach them with Blu-Tack to the backs of the cards (one number on each). Holding up the two cards so the children see only the fronts, say to them: *'Adding A to B will give you 5, multiplying them together will give you 6. What can the numbers be?'* If a child answers correctly, ask others to confirm the answer. Ask the child how the solution was arrived at.

This first example is relatively easy; but as the questions become more difficult, you can introduce a strategy for checking systematically. For example, after asking the question *'Adding A to B will give you 10, multiplying them together will give you 16. What can the numbers be?'*, get the children to list all the possible addition bonds of 10 (ie 1 + 9, 2 + 8, 3 + 7, 4 + 6, 5 + 5). They can work through these in turn until they spot the pair that gives the required product.

After each question has been correctly answered, replace the two numbers on the backs of the cards with another pair. Other questions might include:

● *'Adding A to B will give you 9, multiplying them together will give you 14. What can the numbers be?'* (7 and 2.)
● *'Adding A to B will give you 9, multiplying them together will give you 18. What can the numbers be?'* (6 and 3.)
● *'Adding A to B will give you 11, multiplying them together will give you 30. What can the numbers be?'* (6 and 5.)
● *'Adding A to B will give you 10, multiplying them together will give you 24. What can the numbers be?'* (6 and 4.)
● *'Adding A to B will give you 12, multiplying them together will give you 32. What can the numbers be?'* (8 and 4.)

The children can then make up their own A and B puzzles to try out with the class.

MULTISTEP AND MIXED OPERATIONS

DISCUSSION QUESTIONS
● *How did you find the answer?*
● *How did you make up your own question?*

VARIATION
Try finding a pair of unknowns given subtraction and multiplication facts. For example:
● *'Subtracting A from B will give you 1, multiplying them together will give you 12. What can the numbers be?'* (3 and 4.)
● *'Subtracting A from B will give you 2, multiplying them together will give you 15. What can the numbers be?'* (3 and 5.)
● *'Subtracting A from B will give you 4, multiplying them together will give you 21. What can the numbers be?'* (3 and 7.)

WHAT'S MY NUMBER?

†† *Whole class*
🕐 *20 minutes, several times over a fortnight*

AIM
To explore strategies for using inverses to find unknowns.

WHAT TO DO
Start with a short warm-up, asking questions involving a single operation:
● *'I'm thinking of a number; when I add 7 to it I get 15. What's my number?'* (8)
● *'I'm thinking of a number; when I subtract 8 from it I get 5. What's my number?'* (13)
● *'I'm thinking of a number; when I multiply it by 3 I get 12. What's my number?'* (4)
● *'I'm thinking of a number; when I divide it by 2 I get 7. What's my number?'* (14)

Ask the children to talk about the strategies used to solve these problems, drawing out their awareness of the relationships between addition and subtraction and between multiplication and division. When the children are confident in discussing these ideas, move on to questions involving two operations:
● *'I'm thinking of a number; when I add 2 to it and then multiply by 3 I get 18. What's my number?'* (4)
● *'I'm thinking of a number; when I multiply it by 4 and then subtract 3 I get 5. What's my number?'* (2)
● *'I'm thinking of a number; when I subtract 3 and then divide it by 2 I get 10. What's my number?'* (23)
● *'I'm thinking of a number; when I divide it by 3 and then add 2 to it I get 5. What's my number?'* (9)

Again, encourage the children to articulate their strategies. In the first two or three sessions keep the numbers small, as the underlying principle is the most important thing; as the children become more confident, you can gradually increase the range of numbers used.

DISCUSSION QUESTIONS
● *If the answer is 6 after I have added 2, what should I do to get back to the original?*
(Keep the numbers small and draw out the fact that addition and subtraction are inverse operations.)
● *If the answer is 8 after I have multiplied by 2, what should I do to get back to the original?*
(Again, keep the numbers small and draw out the fact that multiplication and division are inverse operations.)

EXTENSION
In small groups, children can set their own 'What's my number?' puzzles for each other.

THE MAGIC BOXES

†† *Whole class*
🕐 *20 minutes, several times over a fortnight*

AIMS

To practise strategies for addition and multiplication in the context of money. To recognise the distinct effect of each operation.

YOU WILL NEED

A board or overhead projector.

WHAT TO DO

IN $\boxed{\times 2} \to \boxed{+ 3}$ OUT

Draw this diagram on the board or an overhead projector transparency.

Tell the children that they will start with a certain amount of money, which is then changed by each 'magic box' that it passes through. Work through an example with the class, for instance: 2p in produces 7p out; 3p in produces 9p out; 8p in produces 19p out.

Ask the children to copy the diagram on to paper, replacing '× 2' and '+ 3' with other pairs of operations. Examples could include: × 3 + 1; × 4 + 2; × 5 + 3; × 10 + 4.

DISCUSSION QUESTION

Which pairs of numbers have the greatest effect on the amount of money?

VARIATIONS

Try with other operations, for example:

IN $\boxed{\times 5} \to \boxed{- 2}$ OUT

IN $\boxed{\div 2} \to \boxed{+ 4}$ OUT

EXTENSIONS

● Try with three boxes, each containing a different operation. For example:

IN $\boxed{\times 2} \to \boxed{- 2} \to \boxed{+ 10}$ OUT

● The children could design their own 'magic money-changing boxes'. Can they create a set of two or three boxes guaranteed to produce more than £1 for any starting amount? Can they create a set of two or three boxes guaranteed to produce less than the starting amount?
● Investigate the effects of reversing the operations. For example, instead of × 2 + 3, try + 2 × 3. Try this for different number pairs. Does adding first always produce a larger result?

DARTBOARD 2

†† *Whole class, then groups*
🕐 *20 minutes, several times over a fortnight*

AIM

To reinforce strategies for combining doubles and trebles of small numbers.

YOU WILL NEED

A board or overhead projector; several copies of photocopiable page 61.

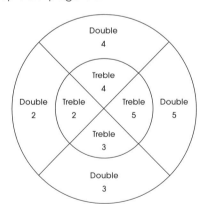

WHAT TO DO

Work through 'Dartboard 1' (page 28) with the children to set the context for, and establish the basic format of, this activity. Draw the dartboard shown above on the board, or make up an overhead projector transparency using the blank grid on photocopiable page 61. Ask the children to find possible ways of scoring a range of answers (for example, all the numbers between 12 and 30)

with three darts. They may use the same section of the board more than once, but all the darts must score. The emphasis should be on speed, so after a couple of minutes stop and pool the results.

Use the blank grid to create alternative number sets for different groups to explore the range of possible scores. (Have the same numbers in the double and treble sections.) Children can use three counters or cubes to mark the numbers they are trying in each turn. Some possible number sets to use are:

- the even numbers from 2 to 8;
- the odd numbers from 1 to 7 or from 3 to 9;
- multiples of 5 (ie 5, 10, 15, 20).

DISCUSSION QUESTIONS
- *How did you calculate your darts? How did you check them?*
- *Can you use one solution to help find another? (For example: treble 4, treble 3 and treble 2 make 25, so moving the dart on treble 4 to double 4 will make 21.)*
- *If all three darts are on trebles or doubles, is there an easier way to find the total? (For example: treble 5, treble 3 and treble 2 will be the same as treble 10 (since 5 + 3 + 2 = 10).*

VARIATIONS
- Allow darts to 'miss', counting 0 as one of the possible scores.
- Have different 'double' and 'treble' numbers.

LET'S GET MEASURED

†† *Whole class, then groups*
🕐 *25 minutes, several times over a term*

AIM
To use different operations in handling information in the context of measurement.

YOU WILL NEED
For each group: rulers, metre sticks, tape measures, paper strips, paper and pencils.

WHAT TO DO
Ask the children to estimate how many times bigger the circumference of their head is than the span of their hand. Demonstrate how to use paper strips to determine each measure. An approximate answer can be obtained by comparing paper strips: one representing the circumference of the head, one the handspan. Alternatively use a tape measure for both, divide one by the other using a calculator and round the answer to the nearest whole number. (It is usually 3.)

Other questions to explore might include:
- *'If all the class handspans were put in a line, would it reach across the classroom?'*
- *'How many of any particular child's handspan would be needed?'*
- *'What is the average (ie **mean**) handspan or head circumference? How many are bigger than that? How many are smaller?'*
- *'What is the difference between the largest and the smallest handspan in the class?'*
- *'If all the head circumferences were added together, what would the total figure be? If that was the head circumference of a giant, how tall might he be?'*

In the first session, this work should be teacher-led; in subsequent sessions, using other body measures, the children can work at similar problems in groups. A good strategy would be to draw up a list of similar questions for the children to answer, but give them opportunities to set their own problems too.

DISCUSSION QUESTIONS
- *How can we measure that? (For example, the circumference of your head.)*
- *What do you need to do (ie which operation on which facts) to solve that problem?*
- *(In response to an estimate, such as how many handspans across the classroom.) Why do you think that?*

VARIATIONS
Other body measures that could be used for data collection and comparison include:
- reach and stride;
- circumferences of waist and lower leg;
- height and foot length.

EXTENSION
The children could use a computer to create a database of all their information.

MAKE UP THE NUMBERS

†† *Pairs, then groups* ⏲ *20 minutes*

AIMS

To reinforce strategies for combining multiples. To work systematically.

YOU WILL NEED

For each pair: a supply of Unifix cubes.

WHAT TO DO

Working in pairs, the children should select two colours of Unifix cubes to use. With one colour, they should make three-cube lengths; with the other, four-cube lengths. They should then join these in any order and number, to investigate what totals can be made up by combining different numbers of 3s and/or 4s. For example, two 4 lengths make 8; two 3 lengths and one 4 make 10; two 4 lengths and one 3 make 11; three 4 lengths make 12. Set the children the task of finding combinations to make all the numbers up to 20 or 30, using 3s and/or 4s only. Encourage the children to record their answers in a systematic way, either pictorially or in numerical form. Pairs of children should compare and combine their solutions in groups to make up a complete set.

In a later session, the children can try the same activity with other number pairs: try 2s and 5s, 3s and 5s, 4s and 5s, 3s and 7s and so on.

DISCUSSION QUESTIONS

● *How did you find the right combination of numbers for that total?*
● *Are there different ways of making some of the totals?*
● *Are there any totals that cannot be made?*

VARIATION

Use Cuisenaire or colour factor rods instead of Unifix cubes.

EXTENSIONS

● The children could use the writing frame on photocopiable page 64 to reflect on their strategies.
● The children can be shown how to record their solutions in a formal way, using brackets. For example:

$17 = (3 \times 3) + (2 \times 4)$

Figure 2

THE MATHS OCTOPUS

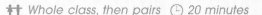

†† *Whole class, then pairs* ⏲ *20 minutes*

AIMS

To encourage flexible use of the four operations. To develop strategies for checking addition, subtraction, multiplication and division, such as using inverses.

YOU WILL NEED

A board or overhead projector; photocopiable page 64 (optional).

WHAT TO DO

First work through an example with the whole class (or group). Draw up a picture of an octopus with a target number marked on it, as in Figure 2. In this example, the target number is 6. The task for the children is to find eight calculations (one for each tentacle) that have the answer 6. At least one tentacle should represent each of the four operations. Solutions for 6 might include: $3 + 3$, $5 + 1$, $16 - 10$, $10 - 4$, 2×3, 6×1, $12 \div 2$, $30 \div 5$.

When the children are used to the format of this activity, they can work in pairs with different target numbers. Suggest that they try 10, 12, 16, 20, 50 or 100; or let them choose their own challenges.

Encourage the children to check that their chosen number sentences are accurate. Observe their strategies for checking: do they use inverses, for example?

Following discussion, the children could use the writing frame on photocopiable page 64 to reflect on their strategies.

DISCUSSION QUESTIONS
● *What is a good way to check that calculation?*
● *Which operation do you find easiest/hardest to work with? Why?*

VARIATION
To simplify the task, let the children work initially with only two operations: either addition and multiplication or subtraction and division.

NUMBER CHAINS

†† *Whole class, then pairs* ⏲ *20 minutes*

AIMS
To reinforce strategies for halving. To practise making predictions and observing patterns.

WHAT TO DO
In this activity, the children will choose a number between 10 and 50 and generate a number chain based upon two rules:
1. *If the number is even, divide it by 2.*
2. *If the number is odd, add 1.*
The sequence ends when 1 is reached.

Work through an example: starting with 27 produces the chain 27 – 28 – 14 – 7 – 8 – 4 – 2 – 1, which is eight numbers long.

Set the children the challenge of working in pairs to find a starting number that produces a longer chain than this. They should make a prediction before starting the calculations. (At this level, they can be expected to predict that the highest numbers produce the longest chains.) A good way for a pair to work might be for each child to take turns using a calculator while the other calculates mentally. They should then work through the sequence again, noting down how many numbers were in the chain. (The longest chain is actually twelve numbers long, when the starting number is 33.)

DISCUSSION QUESTIONS
● *Which numbers are easy to find half of without a calculator?*
● *What patterns do you notice towards the end of each sequence?*

VARIATIONS
● Subtract 1, instead of adding 1, when the numbers are odd. Will the same starting number still produce the longest chain? (33 now produces a chain only seven numbers long; the longest chain using this rule is ten numbers long, starting with 31.)
● Add 3, instead of adding 1, when the numbers are odd. Will all the chains finish at 1? (Hint: try 27.)

EXTENSION
Extend the range of starting numbers to include numbers up to 100.

MULTISTEP AND MIXED OPERATIONS

MULTISTEP AND MIXED OPERATIONS

THE GREAT FUNCTION GAME

†† *Pairs* ⏱ *20 minutes*

AIM
To use different operations in quick succession.

YOU WILL NEED
For each pair: a copy of the race grid (photocopiable page 60) and two dice each marked 2, 2, 3, 3, 4, 4. (Modify ordinary dice with small labels or make up spinners.) Each player also needs a counter or marker.

WHAT TO DO
The children play in pairs. They take turns to throw both dice, determining their score by first multiplying the two dice scores, then adding them together and then finding the difference between the two totals. This number determines how many places along the track the player moves. For example:

> Player A throws a 4 and a 2. Since 4 × 2 = 8 and 4 + 2 = 6, the score is 8 − 6 = 2.
> Player B throws two 3s. Since 3 × 3 = 9 and 3 + 3 = 6, the score is 9 − 6 = 3.

Players make their way along the race track, with the winner being the first to reach or pass 100.

DISCUSSION QUESTIONS
● *What are the best/worst combinations to get?*
(Two 4s give a score of 8. Two 2s give a score of 0.)
● *Which scores can you get? Which ones are impossible?*
(0, 1, 2, 3, 5 and 8 are possible; 4, 6 and 7 are impossible.)

VARIATIONS
● Start at 100 and move backwards – the first player to get back to 1 wins.
● Play the same game on a 0–100 number line.

EXTENSION
Use two ordinary (1–6) dice with the same rules. Note that if one of the dice scores 1 then overall there will be a negative score. For example, throwing a 1 and a 4 results in a score of – 1 since 1 × 4 = 4 and 1 + 4 = 5; in this instance, the player should move backwards on the track.

SWEETSHOP

†† *Small groups* ⏱ *20 minutes*

AIMS
To use operations in combination. To practise strategies for checking answers.

YOU WILL NEED
For each child: a price list (see Figure 3); a pen; photocopiable sheet 64 (optional). For each group: one (ordinary) dice; some counters.

Figure 3

SWEETSHOP
Chews – 2p each
Gob stoppers – 3p each
Giant jellies – 4p each
Pink uglies – 5p each

WHAT TO DO
The children play in small groups. Each child starts with £1 and will have one opportunity to buy each of the sweets, working her/his way down the price list. First, they should each throw the dice to determine how many chews they can buy, recording that number on their price list alongside the total cost. For example if the first child throws a 4, then '4 = 8p' is recorded alongside 'Chews – 2p each'. After they have all thrown for chews they should take it in turns to throw for gob stoppers, then giant jellies, then pink uglies. After throwing for all four types of sweet, each child should calculate a) the total number of sweets that he/she has bought and b) how much money he/she has left. Children should swap papers to check each other's accounting.

There are two winners at the end of the round: the child who has bought the most sweets and the child who has the most money left. Each winner gets a counter. The group play again, starting with £1 each. The overall winner is the child with the most counters after (for example) five rounds, or the first child to collect (for example) five counters.

After discussion, the children can reflect individually on their strategies using the writing frame on photocopiable page 64.

DISCUSSION QUESTIONS
● *Roughly how much do you have left?*
(Encourage children to approximate rather than calculate in the first instance.)
● *How did you check the answers?*

VARIATION
Calculate the amount of money remaining after each purchase.

EXTENSIONS
● Increase the number of items on the list.
● Increase the starting sum.
● Note that using the price list in Figure 3 it is impossible to run out of money, even if a 6 is thrown each time. A possible extension is to increase the sweet costs such as to make 'going broke' a possibility, with no more purchases being allowed if this point is reached.

GET CLOSER

✝✝ *Small groups* ⏱ *25 minutes*

AIMS
To practise combining operations. To use knowledge of number facts in relation to the four operations.

YOU WILL NEED
For each group: three dice; paper and pencils.

WHAT TO DO
Children in the group take it in turns to choose any number between 1 and 50 and to throw the three dice. All of the children in the group (individually) now have to combine the dice numbers, using any of the four operations, to get *as close as possible* to the target number. All three dice have to be used once.

The child whose solution is closest wins the round and scores 1 point. If two or more children have the same winning solution, or solutions that are equally close to the target, then they each score 1 point. Play for a pre-determined number of

rounds (ten rounds should take about 25 minutes). If necessary, use a sand-timer or stop-clock to restrict the time taken for each round; start with a three-minute limit, then gradually reduce the time.

It may be useful to work through some examples with the group first, such as:
Child A chooses the target 37 and throws a 6, a 3 and a 4.
Child A $4 \times 6 = 24$ and $24 + 3 = 27$
Child B $3 + 4 = 7$ and $7 \times 6 = 42$
Child C $3 + 6 = 9$ and $9 \times 4 = 36$
Child C is the closest.

Child B now chooses the target 10 and throws a 3, a 6 and a 5.
Child A $6 + 5 = 11$ and $11 - 3 = 8$
Child B $6 \times 5 = 30$ and $30 \div 3 = 10$
Child C $5 \times 3 = 15$ and $15 - 6 = 9$
Child B is the closest.

DISCUSSION QUESTIONS
● *How did you decide which operations to use?*
● *How did you check the answers?*

VARIATIONS
● Have one of the group acting as an adjudicator; this person can also select the target number and roll the dice in each round.
● Have target numbers on pre-prepared cards that are then selected randomly.
● Play in teams of two within the groups, rather than individually.

EXTENSIONS
● The children could use the writing frame on photocopiable page 64 to reflect on their strategies.
● Play with four dice and target numbers up to 100.
● Allow dice numbers to be combined as 'tens' and 'units' as well as being used as single numbers; in the first example above, an exact solution could then be found by combining the 4 with the 3 to make 43 and subtracting the 6 to make 37.

RACE GRID

100	99	98	97	96	95	94	93	92	91
81	82	83	84	85	86	87	88	89	90
80	79	78	77	76	75	74	73	72	71
61	62	63	64	65	66	67	68	69	60
60	59	58	57	56	55	54	53	52	51
41	42	43	44	45	46	47	48	49	50
40	39	38	37	36	35	34	33	32	31
21	22	23	24	25	26	27	28	29	30
20	19	18	17	16	15	14	13	12	11
1	2	3	4	5	6	7	8	9	10

DARTBOARD

DEVELOPING MENTAL MATHS

ARROW CARDS

1 0 0		1 0		1
2 0 0		2 0		2
3 0 0		3 0		3
4 0 0		4 0		4
5 0 0		5 0		5
6 0 0		6 0		6
7 0 0		7 0		7
8 0 0		8 0		8
9 0 0		9 0		9

PHOTOCOPIABLE

DEVELOPING MENTAL MATHS

NUMBER LINES

0
10
20
30
40
50
60
70
80
90
100

0
100
200
300
400
500
600
700
800
900
1000

63

DEVELOPING MENTAL MATHS

MENTAL MATHS WRITING FRAME

Name _____ Date _____

Today we...

This is what we used...

This is how I did some of the calculations...

What I liked about this activity...

DEVELOPING MENTAL MATHS